Peter Mandel

ESOGETICS

The Sense and Nonsense
of Sickness and Pain

Energetik Verlag GmbH - Sulzbach/Taunus

Peter Mandel

ESOGETICS

The Sense and Nonsense
of Sickness and Pain

© Energetik-Verlag GmbH, Sulzbach/Taunus, 1993
Al rights reserved.

Cover: Siegfried Janusch
Design and Layout: Grafik & Media, Kelkheim/Ts.
Translation: S. Kristen and J. Allanach
Printed by: Freiburger Grafische Betriebe

Printed in Germany
ISBN 3-925 806-71-7

TABLE OF CONTENTS

ESOGETIC THERAPIES

In this book, treatments are found on the following pages:

PREFACE

When I first used the new word Esogetics publicly, in lectures and seminars at the end of 1987, I could not envision that this word I had created would, after such a short time, become a standard term — and not only for insiders.

Esogetics was, I sensed, the canopy to encompass my thought-model.

Based on EEA (Energy Emission Analysis), Colorpuncture, Acu-Impulse therapy, Induction therapy and Color-Sound therapy had already come into being. With the development, understanding and clarification of the Esogetic Model, all these separate methods found their common roof.

Esogetics, as I shall elaborate upon later, is the merger of the esoteric wisdom of life with the energetic principles of life's processes.

In my therapeutic work, in recognizing and treating illness, many new perspectives arose out of this synthesis. I also saw I was better and better able to show ill people the meaning of their sicknesses, and to encourage them to look into that which is making them unwell.

Once one accepts dimensions that are as yet un-proven, Esogetics is totally logical and amazingly simple. That's why I have such a strong inner urge to share it with as many people as possible.

This book hopes to encourage men and women to take more responsibility for themselves and for their health. At the same time, I want to show ways in which one can become aware of this responsibility, and the means with which this responsibility can be fulfilled.

Looking into the sense and nonsense of sickness and pain can lead to the experience and realization of the self.

I would be pleased if, with this book, I were to succeed in stimulating that reflection which leads to insights, to fresh beginnings and to spiritual awakening.

Bruchsal, August 1991   Peter Mandel

ESOGETICS
AN ATTEMPT TO FORMULATE A DEFINITION

Have you ever heard the word "Esogetics"? No? It's no wonder: the word really doesn't exist. Actually, I created it myself.

But what does it mean? The prefix *eso* may already prompt most readers to associate it with the word "esoteric". The thought may arise that here, once again, is another new esoteric doctrine of salvation or some other concept from the beyond. Esogetics is none of these, even if the word may sound like it.

Esogetics, as such, is a new creation, composed of the syllable *eso* from esoteric and *getic* from energetic.

Esogetics is the effort to combine, on the one hand, the heritage of human wisdom with the findings of bioenergetics and modern biophysics, on the other. By using a logical model, Esogetics demonstrates a synthesis of these two entities, making it possible to grasp the philosophical.

The term "esoterics" combines the oldest philosophies and teachings of human wisdom, the primeval knowledge of man's existence and the laws of the cosmos.

At present, the world is full of societies and circles who adorn themselves, in one way or another, with esoteric attributes. A large number of "trainings" and "paths to realization" are offered. As a rule, however, these are all doomed to failure, because esoterics is not a discipline that can be learned or grasped rationally. Understanding esoterics means developing, experiencing and realizing the self.

As a means of turning in, esoterics cannot be taught. It is difficult enough to describe it and impossible to define it exactly. In light of the fact that each human being in this world is unique, this is clear. No two human beings are alike, neither on a mental, spiritual nor physical level. Whatever, in our innermost depths, we comprehend as truth is always our own understanding, always our own reality.

Similarly, Dethlefsen, who certainly set criteria with his books, writes that esoterics is neither a field of knowledge nor a collective term for any facts or formulas. It is, rather, a path. And that path exists inside every human being.

Many people, however, are neither able nor willing to recognize this. These people are not ready to take the trouble to realize themselves, because that would mean abandoning their cherished habits and patterns of behavior. First of all, it would mean letting go of what we call "guilt projection". Ordinarily, somebody or something else is always responsible for any frustration or unrest, any fear or phobia, any aggression or difficulty; in short, for all our emotions.

If we ask ourselves, "What do all these problems, worries and fears have to do with me? What do all these mean for me?" then, without fail, we will come to the conclusion that the individual himself is the creator of his immediate environment. It only appears that joy and suffering, fear and panic, happiness and contentment come from the outside. The point is: we all create these things within ourselves. Everything that constitutes the character and feelings of a person, every contact with his surroundings, emanates from the person himself.

No one would get idea to hit himself constantly on the head with a hammer — yet most people have gone through this sort of learning process. They know it is painful to be hit by a hammer and, because they know this, try to avoid such pain.

If we substitute the word "hammer" with "anger - aggression - stress", it is astonishing that such a large number of people expose themselves again and again to suffering and pain. They are not aware of the fact that they, exclusively, are responsible for their anger, fear and aggression; that, while they look outside for the causes of these emotions, they are inflicting this pain and suffering on themselves; and that, finally, from this, their bodies become sick. Things would be so easy if we were able to understand that it is we ourselves who make us sick, that it is we who disturb and destroy ourselves, and our environment. If each man could understand that he, as an individual, is nothing but a cell in the organism of the earth, then the desire to destroy all other cells/humans, who, in principle, fulfill the same function, would cease.

At first glance, this is a complicated approach. It will, however, become clearer and simpler the more closely we examine it. The more we understand the principle, the simpler and clearer becomes the path upon which we have to walk.

For every human being, the realization of esoteric wisdom can become a path; and like any other path, this path also leads to a certain goal. The search for this goal, however, has to start from within. At the same time, the end of this path will be a beginning. This means coming back to the divine principle; it means overcoming all polarities and gathering the courage to develop towards one's own perfection. Good and bad, guilt and innocence, tension and relaxation — polarities this dimension and this world need to exist — must be surmounted in order to attain the final goal of union with the divine.

Dethlefsen writes that esoterics is the preserver of the sum total of all mankind's knowledge, even though it often disagrees with the beliefs of modern science. Even the most superb discovery, one worthy of a Nobel Prize, is not based on new realizations: the sum of all knowledge is constant and has, at any given time, always been in existence. Everything that has ever been discovered is always here, and has always been here.

Accordingly, the esoteric standpoint is diametrically opposed to the scientific, because if all knowledge is here and has always been here, then in order to realize it, man has to develop towards this knowledge.

Anything new that man is able to discover, understand and formulate is dependent on an idea that comes into being suddenly. It is worth noting that, originally, the term "dis-cover" meant to find something already in existence. And this exactly reinforces my point.

However, since our polar thinking needs to originate somewhere, the question arises, "Who or what gives rise to these ideas, and where does the underlying information come from?"

One is frequently tempted to accept chance as an explanation; however, where did the idea come from, and who or what is behind all of this? The answer to this question could be that all things ever thought and discovered are nothing but the sum total of all knowledge, of knowledge that is always there, and that whosoever hits on one idea or the other is a channel for things that already exist.

The ancestor of esoterics is thought to be Hermes Trismegistos, a priest and initiate of ancient Egypt. Controversy surrounds whether or not he really existed; however, the fact is that esoteric teaching — also called Hermetic philosophy — is based on fifteen theses which Hermes Trismegistos is said to have written. These fifteen theses represent the quintessence of all knowledge. In them, all the knowledge to which mankind will ever have access is summarized.

In relation to the thoughts formulated in this book, the most important thesis of Hermes Trismegistos is: "As above, so below". On the basis of this thesis we can state the following: macrocosm equals microcosm; heaven equals earth; as inside, so outside; and so on. This also means that the same laws govern everywhere, that life appears and

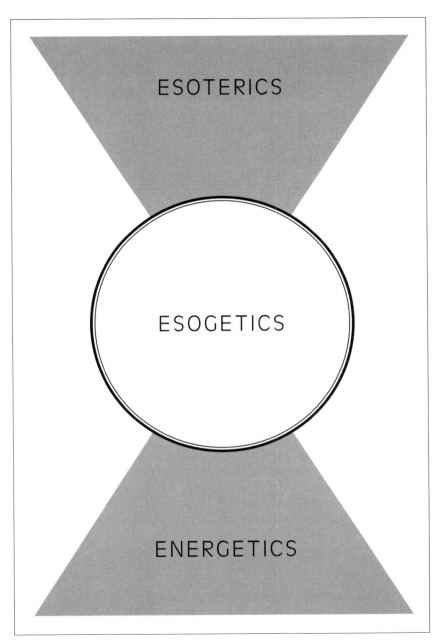

ESOTERICS

ESOGETICS

ENERGETICS

The Esogetic Principle

disappears in accordance with the same eternal laws.

The subtle or non-material part of my Esogetic Model is represented by the Hermetic philosophy. It constitutes the upper half of a model in which two pyramids or triangles stand with tips opposing, mirroring each other. The lower part of this model symbolizes the most recent understandings of biophysics, but it also symbolizes the traditional philosophies of the various cultures, insofar as they concern life and the body.

In this context I would like to refer to the energy model of traditional Chinese medicine and, as well, descriptions of the circulating life energy known as *prana*. Under different names and independent of specific healing methods, these have been found in a number of cultures. All these possibilities are summarized and assigned to the lower triangle.

Therefore, in my Esogetic Model, the two tips stand directly opposite one another. On the top are the teachings of human wisdom; on the bottom are the thought models of bioenergetics and their significance in the treatment of the ill.

At the melting point of these two triangles, something new comes into being: Esogetics.

Esogetics takes the symbolic teachings of esoterics seriously and tries to apply them to man in a tangible way. This happens through logical explanations of what the individual biological systems represent, and what meaning they have in actual practice.

All practical therapeutic methods use one common medium to communicate healing impulses to the human being, and this medium is the outer covering of the body, the skin. All influences, no matter whether they come from within or without, are recorded on the skin.

For me, this statement is not only true for all bodily irregularities, but also for everything that affects the reactions of one's body, mind and spirit. This means that, on the one hand, everything is written down on the skin, exactly as in a book, and need only be deciphered. On the other hand, we can also draw the conclusion that if the "text" is not correct, then the whole pattern of response must also be different. Natural therapy systems have their special methods to re-balance these altered programs.

In the course of this book, my concern is to present these ideas and to substantiate them with examples from my own practice. In this, I shall let myself be guided by the first esoteric law, "As above, so below".

Let us now look at bioenergetics in general.

There cannot be one total, absolute knowledge. An obvious reason for this is that man moves forward in the stream of time. And on his path, he bases new discoveries on realizations that he has made previously. This constantly recurring process demonstrates that it makes no sense to believe that the methods of exact science can, at any one time, ever comprise total knowledge.

For example, what right do some representatives of so-called exact science have to deny the faculty of thinking to people who are not academically trained? Often it is precisely these "simple" people who have ideas and concepts that change the world. And often it is exactly these ideas that can lead a rigid science onto new paths. Nor is this process going to change in the future. Thought and development in bioenergetics, over the last fifty years in particular, have been contributed by people who did not belong to the medical/scientific establishment.

Even today, medicine rejects the term "energy" as the driving force and overriding principle behind all life forms. This is amazing, because it is common knowledge that without energy, without this impulse, without information, life would not be possible. Matter is not the prerequisite for life; rather, life is the prerequisite for matter. Therefore, before matter — only another form of energy, according to Planck — something must exist which includes matter in the life process.

Cultures of this world have pondered this "something" and have found answers to suit themselves and their corresponding times.

All cultures begin with the assumption that there is an energy circulating in everything that lives, and that this, in itself, is the prerequisite for life. According to modern findings, this energy carries information which it transports to the separate sectors of matter, based on their particular affinity. Living matter will then react in accordance with the information held.

This realization is essential for human life. Cells and organs belong to matter, to the lower pole of life's hierarchy. This means they react to information in some way or other, and that they must follow the incoming information carried by the energy. And again the question arises as to where this information comes from, as to who or what gives this information, and according to what criteria are the reactions formed as result of this information?

Let us remember the Hermetic law "As above, so below". If we accept this law as a basis, then the cell cannot only be a performing agent. We know that all the information of life is contained in each cell.

The sensational experiment of the biologist Gordon, who removed the content of a frog's ovum and replaced it with material from an intestine cell, and then induced this cell to divide, has confirmed that each cell carries the overall program of the organism. From one intestine cell, a fertile frog was created! This miracle — the creation of a clone — is the proof.

When a person is born, this life that has just come into being carries completely detailed information, according to a fixed plan. Development, growth, and all other functions are pre-programmed. How can one then doubt that the program of one's own life-course exists in a structured matrix? Even today, however, this still sounds too metaphysical to be acceptable.

Imagine that each evolutionary stage is pre-programmed at the time of birth. Then each person's entire life-path would be pre-recorded from the very beginning. Our intellectual brain, our mind, cannot conceive of this so easily. In spite of this, we consistently know and sense that there is something in us that guides us, yet eludes our mind's grasp. This "something" is certainly there, and the analytical mind strives to understand it.

Each individual's program can be compared to a "skeleton agreement" that must be filled with life. Man is an open system, a system that has to develop. From birth to physical death, he has an inner urge to fulfil l this program. A person's body, his cells, organs and systems, help him to reach these pre-programmed goals, but they are not responsible for the program itself, neither for the life-task nor for the goal.

The body is nothing but a means of reaching a goal; it therefore fulfills the function of a tool. The energy-information system within our physical/material world is constantly performing courier services in order to fulfill our own program. And because we cannot imagine or grasp the concept of this perpetually-flowing energy in our bodies, we find it very difficult, for example, to acknowledge that cells and organs can only respond in ways permitted by the information contained in the energy flow.

Traditional Chinese medicine has based its concept of health and sickness exclusively on an energy system that permeates the entire body. The theory of Chinese medicine operates on the premise that the human body is flooded by a dense network of invisible channels in which the life force, *chi*, is constantly flowing. This *chi*, representing many other terms describing the same force, has been considered as the life-giving energy in nearly all cultures, old and new. The Egyptians,

Hindus, Greeks and Romans, as well as the Gnostic, Neoplatonic, Jewish and early Christian mystics and metaphysicians, all believed in this energy. This life energy, this *chi* — by whatever name it was called — plays a central role in the secret Hermetic esoteric teachings, in alchemy, in the medicine of the Renaissance, and in Humanism.

All races have always described the concept of soul in their own languages by using terms that represent barely perceptible matter: breeze, wind, breath, air, blowing. They derived these pictorial terms from the process of the incoming and outgoing breath.

The realization that life is inseparably linked with breathing, and that the body becomes a corpse without breathing, has led to equating Psyche (breath) and Ios (life). Apparently the people of old found it far easier to deal with the mysterious phenomena of life in a concrete and rational way. They established a mathematical equation that said the difference between a live body and a corpse must be "life", and that the carrier of this life must be a mysterious energy.

The Chinese made it their task to learn about the laws governing the circulation of the life energy in the living body, the laws which make the *chi* present everywhere in the body. Over millennia, it most likely took unbelievably detailed work to determine that the *chi* flows in special channels forming a dense network that permeates the entire body. These channels or meridians connect all parts of the body with each other, forming a network of meridians comparable to an irrigation system. In this system the *chi* circulates, controls and preserves the healthy and normal functioning of the bio-organism.

The normal functioning of the body — health — is guaranteed so long as the *chi* flows harmoniously and is equally balanced, in its appropriate speed and in the right quantity, throughout the invisible network of meridians. Therefore, one feels well and healthy when all meridians are filled with the same amount of *chi*.

If the *chi* is blocked or weakened quantitatively in one or more areas of the body, or even if it comes to a standstill in some places, then there is imbalance. The meridians that are inadequately provided with *chi* are weakened and therefore no longer able to protect against pathogenic or disease-causing agents. These disease-causing agents themselves also use the system of meridians. This will result, for example, in diseases of the internal organs being accompanied by symptoms on the surface of the body or at its extremities; for example, the joints, and so forth. This is approximately how the Chinese Taoists formulated these processes.

In this dimension, everything that we associate with the term "energy" exists in polarity. Thus the Chinese sages imagine a picture in which the yin/yang polarity comes into existence out of the "all-one" or Tsri.

It is only possible to understand the energetic principle through the polarity of yang/yin, plus/minus, order/chaos. Contrary to commonly held opinion, the yin/yang polarity in Taoism does not express any kind of evaluation. Neither does the yang as the male, positive pole, represent good in a moral way, nor does the yin, as the female, negative pole, represent bad. Both poles are value-free. They are mutually dependent and each draws its right to exist from the existence of its counterpart.

Yin stands for the earth, the female, the receptive. Yin is soft, dark, weak, devotional, passive. Yang represents the sky, the male. Yang is creative, productive, impregnating, hard, resistant, aggressive, bright, warm and strong.

These symbols show that, according to the Chinese view, the cosmos is preserved only by the equal values of yin and yang. All parts of this cosmos must submit to the same lawfulness. Yin and yang always swing back into harmony, symmetry and equilibrium. They balance each other out like the pans of a scale. If we think about the cybernetic theory of the cybernetic circle, or about the Gestalt circle in psychology, or the findings of the self-regulation of autonomous nervous systems, then these, in different words, provide a description of the yin/yang polarity.

According to the philosophy of Tao — meaning way, path, or direction — yin and yang are embedded in the bosom of Tao, secure as a clock in its casing, and are forced by the Tao into a ball or two-dimensional circle.

With respect to the individual, Tao is the "being condemned to exist" as formulated by Sartre, or the "being thrown" by Heidegger. But Tao is good, merciful, and loving, like God. Tao is all and everything in the cosmos. It is the law of nature, irrevocable; one has to submit to it without contradiction. Later religions gave different names to the same realization: Jahwe, Adar, or God, whose unfathomable decisions have to be followed without opposition, like the incomprehensible rotation of the Tao.

Western metaphysicians were not the first to develop the thesis that microcosm equals macrocosm, that "As above, so below". More than any other people, the Chinese have long been convinced that the human individual, as a connecting link between heaven and earth, corresponds to the Tao's relation to the cosmos. Accordingly, Taoist philosophy teaches that the all-powerful forces of yin and yang rule over the human being as a whole, as well as over each separate part of the body. For this reason, Chinese healers considered it their foremost task to ensure that the balance of yin and yang was maintained or regained.

As mentioned earlier, the energetic polar thought-model forms the lower part of two triangles or pyramids that mirror each other. The upper part contains the comparable, symbolic thinking of esoterics. If these two parts — which are "one" — touch each other, then, through the flow of power from above and below, something new comes into existence. I call this "something new", Esogetics.

Another way to present this thought is as follows: The esoteric may be described as vertical thinking and the energetic as horizontal thinking. If we put the vertical and the horizontal on top of each other, we get the Esogetic cross. The point where these two principles meet is the origin of the new thinking of Esogetics. Here, esoteric and energetic knowledge merges. Here, a model becomes conceivable.

This model is composed of seven principles which cooperate indivisibly and determine the rhythm of life.

Before I embark upon a detailed presentation and explanation of this model, I wish to include a few reflections on life and the destiny of each individual.

ENERGETICS

ESOTERICS

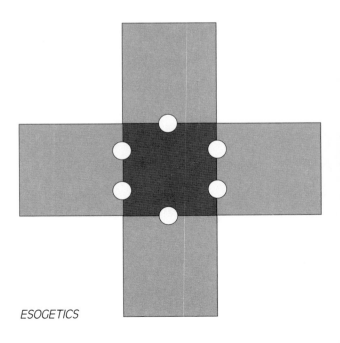

ESOGETICS

18

ESOGETIC GUIDELINE

Looking at man, it would be absurd to try to reduce him to his various biological and physical functions. Too many premonitions, sensations and experiences that transcend the material rule over our lives.

Man moves forward in the stream of time, beginning with his birth and ending with his physical death. The source of his life, however, starts bubbling up much earlier. It arises at the moment of his conception. But what is going on before? And who or what creates life?

When speaking about our bodies, we mostly say "My body is such and such, or has this or that." But who possesses this body? Who is this "me"? Down the ages, philosophers have delved into this question. And, still, the impossibility of finding any scientific proof does not deter people from searching for an answer to this question.

Scientific proofs are always based on past thinking. They define something which has already been explained and understood within the forward thrust of evolving thought. People who cling to the solely scientific always have dogmatic structures. This means that, in this natural progression of thought, the rigidity of their thinking makes them stagnant. Lacking any discernible movement, this stagnation makes them inflexible and rigid. And the resistance to the natural flow and evolution increases in proportion to the degree of their rigidity or dogmatism. Apparently standing on the safe, "proven" side, these people are actually standing in the way of change; they become obstacles in the river of time.

We can never find answers to the questions of the present from outside ourselves. It is always inner impulses, emerging suddenly, which urge men and mankind forward to new thoughts and ideas, to new deeds.

The universe, the planet and human beings also change during the forward motion of time. We all have difficulty experiencing these constant changes, because each of us, in his own way, obstructs the river of time. We therefore try to grasp these changes intellectually, and comprehend them.

It is important to understand that, by reflecting on past experiences and mistakes, we can gain insights that may help us draw the right conclusions. Insight never supports one's fear of evolving. Moreover, one gains insights into a time when one was just as real as one is today or, perhaps, tomorrow.

To be "insightful", therefore, means to "look inside", into one's own past experiences. An insightful person does not become distracted from himself; he does not always look for explanations and blame on the outside. Analyzing himself by projecting the pictures from his past, he understands the flow of time. The outside, then, becomes nothing but a mirror for the promotion of self-analysis and self-realization, opening new horizons in the present and the future. In this way, the value and meaning of life are given a new, more complete dimension.

By looking from the present into past experiences, we are forced to change our standpoint, provided we do not hide behind the protective shield of "Yes, but...": "Yes, but if this had not been the case, I would have reacted differently and I would not have done this"; "Yes, but if my neighbor had been always friendly towards me, I would have never gotten into conflict with him." This process of analyzing one's own life requires the courage to look into the mirror directly and to encounter oneself, and life, unconditionally.

This means I have to be willing to understand "insight" in a positive way — realizing that all unfriendly reactions that come from others, all conflicts, all aggressions and frustrations have their causes in me and only in me. It is the resonance of my ego that determines whether or not I become irritated, annoyed and, ultimately, sick.

If I meet my aggressive partner with love, then I remove the target, and the aggression falls flat. If I give him the feeling that I like him, or maybe even love him, then the aggressiveness will immediately disappear and he will become attuned to my sympathetic vibrations. In this way, life develops a new quality, and a new form of communication emerges.

Approaching another human being does not mean surrendering or sacrificing oneself. Nor does it mean weakness! It means making the effort to meet aggression with love. It becomes, in this way, the message of the Sermon on the Mount translated into action.

Hate and love arise from the same source, just as plus and minus have the same origin. If man has the courage to examine his life without any outside influence, then he has already programmed himself for his new future.

When man observes his own evolution, he gets the impulse to change the "now"; and his life takes on a new quality, especially in relation to looking towards the future. By analyzing his past experiences, he will then start to change his life. In this way he transforms the river of time into something new, into something which would not have been possible without the re-examination of his past.

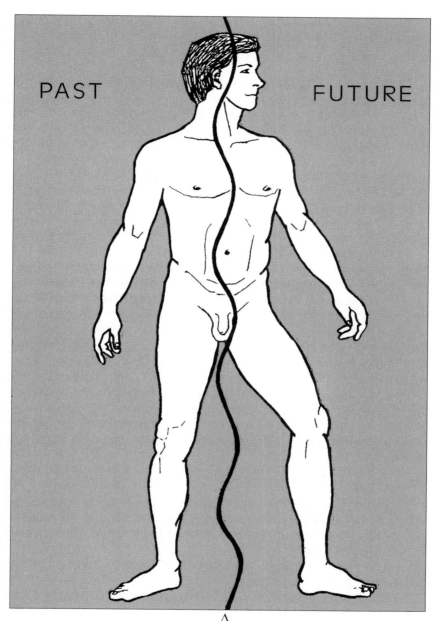

PAST

FUTURE

PRESENT

In summarizing all these standpoints, man's evolution can be defined by the following three terms:

1. CHANGE
Change pre-supposes one must evaluate and question all one has learned and accumulated, thereby analyzing the contents of one's own life. It also means the feeling that "something is not right or no longer fits" must produce an inner urge — resulting in a decision to find a new path or to create one, and then, finally, to walk upon it.

2. MODIFICATION
Modification pre-supposes change. It denotes the moment of conscious, intellectual manifestation of a sensation or an idea. It represents the point when the idea becomes a picture, and when this idea becomes a plan.

At this stage, the will to modify and, therefore, to transform the inner, is dominant. Then the decision is reached whether or not the individual is able to give up the old in order to experience the new.

Anything new is simply a product of the past. This is the reason why, within this dimension, continuous modification is a law. What we consider as truth today; what we often cling to fanatically and dogmatically, is going to be a lie tomorrow.

Modification also means encountering "today's truth" critically and, again and again, having the courage to analyze it. To consciously allow this modification, with no consideration for one's immediate surroundings, courage is required.

This acceptance of the inner self; this recognition that everything must be constantly transformed, is the condition which will then help change to occur.

3. TRANSFORMATION
Transformation on the outside is always the result of transformation on the inside. Everything we see, hear and feel; everything we consider as good or bad on the outside, is the result of transformation in one's own inner life.

Here, the decision to change and modify is absolute. Transformation is the starting point for a new path.

Evolution towards the higher, however, is the goal of all paths that men — or mankind as a whole — walk upon. Looking at this on a solely material plane will lead to the conclusion that this is a desire to be superior to others, to be on top, to be powerful, to rule over others and to impose one's thoughts on them. But, as a whole, transformation means that any epoch mankind lives through is always molded by changes in thinking and the modifications that result. Therefore, it is the will to transform — the will to constantly look for new paths, the will to leave the old behind without forgetting the lessons we have learned — which strengthens our individuality and helps us move forward each moment of our lives.

Change. Modification. Transformation. Why does this process repeat itself infinitely? Why must mankind make so many mistakes, and why must they also keep on happening in the future? When will the solution to this problem bring us freedom, and with it, the salvation of our being?

These are questions with no answer, but still we can sense that the issues of "Where do we come from?" and "Where are we going?" are deeply rooted in our beings, and sometimes, in remembering, the darkness suddenly gives way to the overflooding light of realization and understanding.

We would very much like to cling to these rare moments, to preserve the beauty of this light within ourselves. Even so, we have to keep on traveling, resolving everything again and again. We who are imprisoned in matter have to bring our "I" out of matter and darkness, and into the light.

Max Planck does not believe in any "matter" as such; rather, he considers it another form of energy. Bob Toben describes matter as light imprisoned by gravity. This is a really exciting definition, because it considers light as the ultimate source of all existence.

On the level of the material world, we humans, in our wholeness, are light-beings. We must, and always will, develop towards the absolute light, which we call God.

In this process we are accompanied by light on the outside and as well, if we allow it, by light on the inside. To allow it means not to try to block the light or imprison it; rather, it means we have to "let go". But this gets us into difficulty, because letting go always means giving up those things we cherish.

It is a difficult and demanding task to give up those comforts which often bring frustration and resignation, and, with courage and trust, to let go. Each of us has to come to a decision at this point: to cling or to let go, to stand still or to flow.

We all are subject to the inner impulse to develop towards the higher, towards the light. The extent to which we resist this process is up to each one of us.

WHAT IS DISEASE?

If we look at today's world as a whole, the idea of a disease, of an almost incurable disease, arises automatically. The root of disease, on the outside, in the world, always has its analogy, its cause, on the inside. For man, this means it is he who is making the world sick, because he himself is sick. As with all things, "disease" is a reflection of the inner, and tries, through the principle of resonance, to synchronize or program everything to the same state of being.

Disease is opposite to health. Health is usually associated with joy, happiness and a pain-free life; with having ideas and being able to live them out; with being active and being able to laugh; with being able to perceive and recognize things that others cannot or choose not to see. Disease means frustration, pain, the paralysis of life. It is the opposite of happiness and beauty; it is darkness and death.

It is thought that one is dependent on the other, that if there were no health, we would not know what disease is, and vice versa. However, there is a decisive flaw in our thinking: disease, always, is only the upside-down unreality of life, manifest.

Let us compare a man's life with a pen, an enclosure into which he is born and in which he ends his days. Although the pens of many individual lives border on each other, as in a honeycomb, a man has to accept that he is limited to his own. He has to live in it; he can live only in it.

While he explores his own territory he has many possibilities: he can get to know and enjoy the beauty that surrounds him. He can wander through his own life with open eyes, recognizing and taking note, a well as of the positive, of marshlands and ways that are impassable. However, he can also close his eyes and, by accident, step into a puddle. And instead of reacting and leaving this uncomfortable place immediately, he may remain there and complain about having cold feet, which, in the course of time, will grow colder and colder. Gradually, from bottom to top, the wet, cold feet will dominate his thoughts and feelings.

As time passes, the memory of the beauties of his own pen will fade. He will neither see nor recognize them any more. His whole existence will be reduced to these wet and cold feet. He is imprisoned and blocked: he is sick. Let us now compare this picture with the term "disease".

Long before we recognize it, disease, as such, has already begun. It started at a time we were still experiencing light and beauty. Then, suddenly, in our life, we step into cold water, into a puddle. And instead of recognizing the difference and stepping out of it, we wonder why it has to be us, of all people, who is the victim, who has to experience something so awful!

And the longer we mull over it, the more the idea of happiness

Life's Pen

and beauty recedes into the background. We grow accustomed to the present feeling, complain about the hardship we are experiencing and forget completely what existed before. We get sick — or rather, the body, as the container of our being, gets sick. Everything we are then becomes focused on the body. The river of time stands still, and the blockage and the pressure grows steadily.

In the terms of our analogy, our feet grow colder and colder, until, one day, they fall off.

Remember: the individual pen is only one among others. All are

structured in the same way, even though, fundamentally, there are differences.

We may be lucky, and someone may call to us from the adjoining pen, "Neighbor, you seem to have cold and wet feet." We will answer, "Oh, yes," and go on to describe in detail all the attributes of wet and cold feet. Or, on the other hand, our neighbor may tell us about the beauty of the environment that surrounds us. We, however, are trapped in our cold, wet puddle.

Our neighbor may also provide us with the impetus to overcome the situation. He may say, "Take a step forward." This step can often mean effort, only because we cannot understand that this step forward might help rid us of our cold and wet feet. But if we try; if we make a firm resolution, then we will be able to exchange the wet, dark marsh for the sunny side of life. And then, again, we will be able to see the beauty of our own surroundings.

At first our feet will still be wet and cold. But, soon, we will feel

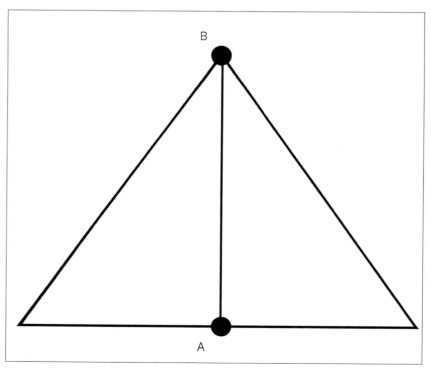

Relationship: Birth (A) - Death (B)

them getting warmer and, slowly, we can start enjoying our redis-covered surroundings. And soon it is going to be dry and warm. Soon, the beauty around us will make us forget the wet, the cold and the dark.

Since our pens contain many such puddles, it may happen, of course, that we get cold feet again and again. Then we will see if we have learned our lesson, and that is, at the first encounter with the "cold", to set out in another direction in search of the warmth and the light. This is how we prevent wet and cold feet and, therefore, sickness.

Seen in this way, disease is walking on a wrong path, on one that has been taken only because the right path could not be recognized.

So, man has three possibilities for traveling his allotted time. Let us imagine, between birth and death, that life takes place within an isosceles triangle. The possibility man is given for traveling this space is indicated by the line between the base (birth) and the apex (death).

Starting one's life path from point A, there are three different ways to reach to life's melting point. First, a person moves directly from

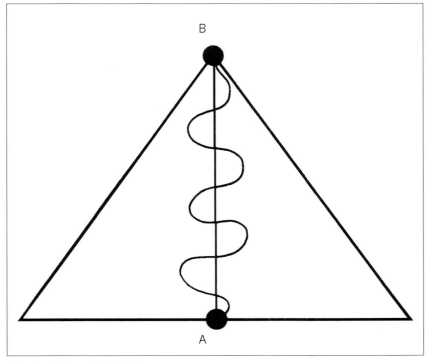

Life Path from (A) to (B)

A to B. Secondly, he wanders from his life's path again and again, but never loses contact with his program or way, which is predetermined.

Thirdly, a person leaves the direct route completely, blunders around, loses his life-line and with this, his life's meaning. After some time he will reach point B. This person will not find an answer to the sum total of his life, nor a resolution to his life's program. As the drawing indicates, again and again he has made contact with his life program; however, could never follow it directly. This means he keeps committing the same mistakes and, therefore, has to deal with the consequences again and again. And if he does not become "insightful"; if he does not recognize and accept the cause of these recurring disturbances, he will destroy himself.

Let us suppose life is a classroom. We are the pupils who must learn in order to move on to the next class. In between, there are examinations to reveal what we have or have not understood. These examinations show what we still need to understand. The final examination —

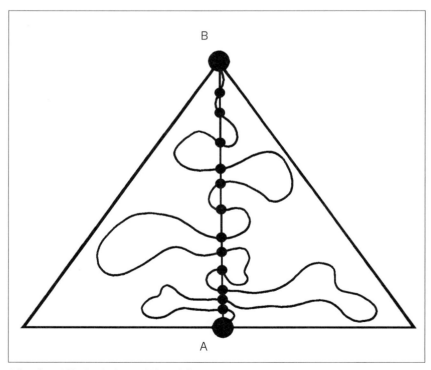

Mistaken Life Path from (A) to (B)

comparable to point B on our life-triangle — will then reveal whether we have learned the lesson of our class or whether we will have to repeat it again.

According to this analogy, this means we will be asked, at the end of our life on earth, about the significance of our past experiences. Will we be satisfied with the essence of what we see, or will we have to admit that everything went wrong?

The final examination is death. Here, at the melting point of life, we will be given the marks we deserve, and whatever remains undone will be noted down.

We who reincarnate again and again, on our return to another time and, perhaps, another place, must first complete, learn and understand what we have not dealt with, before we are allowed and able to proceed on the road towards the highest principle, towards God.

Even though many people do not yet know what to do with this philosophy of life, more and more people of all religions are, in the meantime, becoming aware that the principle of learning and developing from life to life makes sense.

No one who sets out on the path in search of the higher is ever without assistance. All he need do is recognize and accept the help that is available to him. Never before, in the recent evolution of man, have so many indications and possibilities been available; never has there been as much help and support as today.

But this, also, has two sides; this, also, carries the quality of an examination.

If a man who has started on his path with an innocent heart falls back into old patterns of behavior — perhaps saying, "Doctor, it is your fault that I am sick" — then he is distracted from his desired goal and simply marks time.

There is only one single road towards well-being: one's own path. Each human being has to pass his own examinations; he has to travel through his own territory, through his own pen, with all its light and dark aspects. If he lets himself become diverted by the outside, then he will not reach the goal of his class. And becoming diverted means becoming ill.

Disease can also be defined as an impulse for change, an impulse which signals the person, "Analyze yourself and your surroundings. Try to discover and remove the reasons for your stagnation. Gain insights into the past in order to understand and resolve the present and the future."

At this point, however, the biggest self-deception automatically happens, and that is, "I cannot!" But everything we "cannot" can be learned, as long as we really want to.

Comfort often makes it difficult to take a step forward. It takes a lot of strength to step out of this mire of "marking time". It also requires considerable knowledge of the laws of life and the connection between spirit, soul and body.

Literature is full of hints and suggestions as to how to live and act in order to reach certain goals. But this often leads to confusion, because authors suggest many different solutions for any one theme. Each of them is dogmatic, considering his thoughts to be the only right and valid ones. This is how they create dependence in their followers, preventing people from traveling their paths on their own.

Real help is offering the possibility of accompanying the person, in his frustration and trouble, part of the way — and trying to free him from his obstacles and show him new directions, yet allowing him to decide himself which direction he wants to take.

All teachings that are dogmatic and claim to be absolute are wrong and dangerous. Truth remains truth. And the absolute truth remains with God. My truth may be a lie for someone else, and his truth — that he defends as I defend my own — may not be right for me.

"My" and "his" opinion do not resonate together. And this is good, because it is true that there is some vibration of darkness to be found in light, and some vibration of light also exists in darkness. That means that in everything that is wrong in this world, there is always something right, and that in all worldly truths something is always wrong as well. If we accept this; if we recognize this, then we will be helped on our path towards wholeness, on our path towards God.

> *Nature knows neither pip nor skin.*
> *She is all-in-one.*
> *You should examine first of all*
> *whether you are more pip (spirit) or skin (form, body).*

Considering this poem by Goethe, it strikes me as fantastic what a metaphysical attitude this great poet had! If in the life of man, both pip and skin — spirit and form — meet at the center, everlasting joy and contentment result.

It is important for us to experience, through our outer form, the spirit within ourselves. This means it is necessary to recognize ourselves as spirit and be able to love ourselves as we are, in all our light and dark aspects. To look inside means to dare to take the first step in search of the spirit that lives inside each of us. The recognition that, in this dimension, spirit (pip), soul (skin) and body (form) exist in indivisible interdependence, is the ripening of self-knowledge. Nothing is more important than understanding and realizing ourselves.

It is not our environment that determines our lives, but we ourselves. Our thoughts and actions are responsible for our surroundings and for our lives.

The differences in the programs of all human beings unite, ultimately, into one whole, the spirit out of which all egos, personalities and individuals were created and are going to be created. Therefore, the realization of one's own center is the prerequisite for our ability to love one another, to love creation, and to love life.

First of all, we have to find ourselves and love ourselves in order to be able, not only to accept the other in his reality but, ultimately, to love him. On our way towards the highest principle — God — a worthy goal would be to stay in the background without renouncing oneself, to be humble and silent on the outside as well as on the inside, to love the world as it is, and to understand the polarities of good and bad, health and disease, life and death.

Everyone has the impulse to look for happiness and joy outside himself. They cannot be found there, and the reflections we encounter, received from the outside, are called fear, stress, envy, and hate. Fear, because we may fail; stress, because we are swimming against our own current, because we want to be like others; envy, because others are better, more beautiful, bigger, more successful, more powerful than we are. And ultimately hate, because we cannot manage to fulfill the image that, from the outside, we have been led to believe in. The result is disappointment and depression, manifesting, inevitably, in physical exhaustion and disease.

In the spirit-soul-body trinity, my own life has absolute priority. To realize my "self" requires that I embark upon an inner path, that I explore and come to know myself, that I find my center. As soon as I, with sincerity, start on the path towards my core, the more and more I undermine negative behavior patterns such as fear, stress, envy, and hate. With each step I am more at peace in myself, and am able to feel, more purely, the warmth of my heart and love for all life-forms.

The main lesson for each human being should be to rule over himself and not over others. Then all influences coming from the outside can be accepted gratefully. Then we integrate ourselves into the positive flow of information this world so urgently needs.

The next step is meditation, diving deep into the unknown spaces of our own beings. We will discover we have to clear away a lot of "garbage" to come closer to our own center, to our spirit.

This center can also be understood as pure light, as light that exists in the darkness of matter. According to Bob Toben — "matter is light imprisoned by gravity" — the spirit within matter must be understood as light that has to be pried loose and set free.

Man, as a light-being, must turn his awareness towards the light; he must not stay imprisoned in the darkness of matter. If man turns towards this light inside himself, he will rise ever higher and higher. In this process he will leave the dark clouds of fear and frustration far behind. As the golden light in his heart becomes stronger, they will dissolve.

On this journey, light, colors and sounds will accompany him. The deeper he looks inside himself, the lighter and purer he gets until the moment comes when the spirit, or light within his own form is set free. Then he will again be what he was before: a light-being without the burden of a material body.

In explaining my Esogetic Model, which serves to clarify the melting of esoterics and energetics, I start at the very foundation. I am trying to develop an understanding of the functions of the body and their coordination as a basis for learning the "writing", for further thought, and for donning a new skin. In order to be able to recognize the mistakes in our program, and respond to them, we have to decipher this writing.

For this, the next step in the Esogetic Model is required: getting to know the information- and energy-concepts of life. Here, we have to be able to conceive and understand how these form-giving forces have their influence on everything, to the tiniest component.

Ultimately we will come to the point of the transcendental. Here, the power of visualization is needed; here, we can expect to find answers to our life — where it originates and why it exists.

This seven-fold Esogetic Model is a model of vision, a help on the path towards oneself. It is an effort "to experience the pip via the skin." On the one hand, it helps us understand the physical dimension and its functions; on the other, to understand the nature of thoughts, how they arise, what kind of blockages they create and, also, what kind of freedom they can bring. It is a thought-model which invites us to embark upon a journey, through the body, towards the unknown.

By stimulating certain zones and points, one can experience another world — the world of one's own dreams. Through this process, blockages can be recognized and removed.

It may sound illusory or even utopian when I describe the possibilities of experiencing information of the higher spheres of our being through the physical dimension, especially through the skin. However, if one puts it to the test, everything I describe will be experienced. If one follows the instructions I give later on, he will spontaneously experience, on himself, the effects described.

It is always my concern to sharpen our awareness so as to be able to recognize pain as signals pointing to blockages of the entire individual being, signals which make us realize that energy is obstructed and, therefore, information is interrupted. Through the Esogetic Model, we can comprehend the statement of the great German physician Reinhard Voll that pain is the outcry of the tissue for flooding energy, and with it, for flowing information — to put it simply, for each pain there is a reason in the depths of our consciousness. These reasons have to be recognized and resolved. In this regard, I will also produce first attempts at practical proofs to illustrate that disease and pain have meaning.

If we can recognize the meaning hidden behind pain and suffering, we can turn on our heels and abandon the path that leads to the void. If we do not recognize this, then disease and pain become meaningless. Then we have not understood the signal and the message that say, "Turn around, change your actions and realize yourself." Our downfall is predetermined.

The Esogetic Model gives man the possibility to "take himself in hand" — especially in times of apparent health — in order to find and experience the divine energy within. Esogetics is a teaching for all, an offer that needs no circle, no association, no group work, no guru, no priest. Its purpose is to attempt to experience the center through the body.

At this point I would like to start on a journey through the molecules of the Esogetic Model. It is not so important to describe all the details of each individual station. I consider it more important to give an overview of the fantastic possibilities that the concept of Esogetics can impart.

The most important message is the statement that no man on this earth can be "healed" by somebody else. Neither doctor nor naturopath, neither guru nor healer is able to do that. What can be offered as help comes out of the possibilities contained in the therapist's knowledge and strength; however, he can only assist in finding the right path, in putting those seeking help on the right track. Then, everyone must "drive" on his own. The healer of a sick man is that man himself. He alone can heal himself, can come to a state of wholeness — can become "holy".

I claim that my discoveries contribute to the indication of paths that can bring healing to each human being. And by saying "each" human being, I mean all sick people have something in common: each one, as an individual, is on the wrong path, outside his own program.

Esogetics opens up new possibilities for all men. It needs no ideology, because it does not cultivate the inconceivable in order to turn it into a question of faith. On the contrary, Esogetics attempts to make the inconceivable conceivable. All of the paths offered can be investigated immediately and converted into personal experience and, therefore, brought into the context of the individual sickness and the individual pain.

The body, in its wholeness, perceives pain just as the consciousness which should be ruling over this body. Or is it the case that our conscious "I" doesn't even know that which it should be ruling over? This conscious "I", one thinks, is that which I am. Or? Or is it only an assembly of millions of personalities which should be moving forward in time from the moment of birth? Is it not true that the conscious "I" is nothing but a hotch-potch of imprints that we have to experience and live out again and again?

Either out of worry or love, our parents told us repeatedly , "You should not", "You must not", "You have to". At some point, our conscious "I" adopted these parental values, although we can never be as our parents were, or are. There were also grandparents, uncles and aunts, teachers and priests who repeatedly reinforced the messages of our parents. Since everything repeats itself, one day we ourselves will have children to whom we will say, "You should not", etc. This is a vicious circle. Is there a way to get out of this?

We can free ourselves only if we destroy, shake off, and drop the chains of constraint and frustration which prevent us from living our lives, and which draw us into the abyss of disease and death. Only then will we really begin to live.

When a child says, "I have a body", or "My body is sick", then we have to ask who or what is this "I" who possesses this body. There is an entity whose body is sick. This "I" we have to find, to find it in ourselves.

For this, it is necessary to stop for a moment in order to look inside. We will realize suddenly that our conscious mind is deceiving us, and that it distracts us from the program we have brought with us into this world. It will then dawn upon us that what lies behind cannot, in actual fact, be our life. On the other hand, our past experiences have left such deep traces upon us that we are not able to free ourselves — free ourselves to search for our own future and, as well, to live it.

This seems to be a dilemma, yet these past experiences and imprints — even though it may sound paradoxical — were, and still are necessary. They may even be the prerequisites for us, one day, to remember our own program. Perhaps even our difficulties, fears, depressions and physical diseases are nothing but the voice of our higher consciousness urging us to finally walk on our own path in order to find and realize our own program. However, if we remain stuck in our habits; if we take this medicine for our pain and that medicine for our fears, then we will never be happy and free — because pain and fear will always return.

It is a law that everything develops from the fine and subtle to the gross and solid. That means disease can be defined on two levels.

The first is the psychological level. According to the results of diagnostic-scientific apparatuses, the body may be healthy. In this case, a man may feel sick and possibly be in pain, but he is still considered healthy. He must be, because in often endless tests with countless apparatuses no special parameter could be found. Then at point "X" in time, somebody finds the symptom "Y" in some checkup and, suddenly, a person is considered sick.

Shaking his head, he stands there, and is maybe even told that he is too late, even though he has done nothing else year after year but try to find the root cause of his suffering.

Nothing falls out of the blue; everything develops.

Here I remember a story from ancient China: A disciple asks his master, "Master, what is disease?" The master answers, "Disease is a thought."

This clarifies the statements made above and leads to the saying, "That which I think, that I am."

My Esogetics may not be able to explain where a thought comes from, but it may be able to bring us closer to the solution. In this, I am aware of the possible limitations of my thought processes. I also know that my effort to explain can only be a beginning of a new way of thinking, called "Esogetic thinking".

It is, for me also, again and again an amazement how logical are the connections between the Esogetic molecules within the model. The results are tangible and the effects can be experienced by each individual, by sick people as well as by so-called healthy people with their everyday aches and pains.

ESOGETIC MODEL

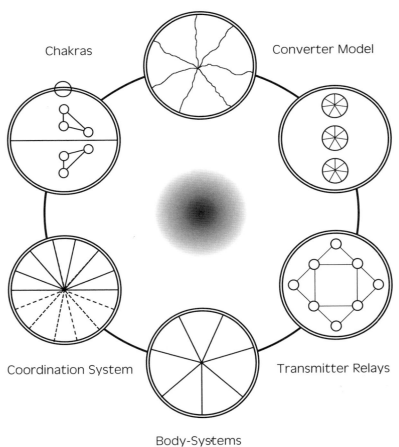

Formative Field

Chakras

Converter Model

Coordination System

Body-Systems

Transmitter Relays

So, therefore, I shall now begin to take the reader on a journey through the magic world of the Esogetic molecules.

My Esogetic Model encompasses seven aspects. Six of them are arranged in an outer circle. I call these six circles in the circle the Esogetic molecules. The seventh aspect lies in the middle and relates in all directions.

In my view, the lower three molecules symbolize the material world. The lowest of them refers to the material body. The left molecule shows the coordination organs of the brain in their totality.

When I observed the coordination of the brain, I chose seven special areas which I named the "Council of Seven". It goes without saying that these seven areas cannot explain the functions of the brain entirely; however, through the way they function we receive valuable information as to how we operate in this world, in this dimension.

The lower right molecule represents a system I have discovered called "The System of the Seven Transmitter Relays." As the name indicates, a transmission occurs here. On the one hand, this means a transfer of power; on the other, it indicates permeability and filtering. As I see it, in our lives, it means that nothing can pass through this system which does not fit the individual program of the person concerned. The system of the Transmitter Relays represents Cerberus, the guardian at the gate of our conscious life.

So, the three lower molecules belong to the material world, where they have their assigned place and task. They represent gross matter, whereas the three upper molecules represent subtle matter.

In the fourth molecule on the left side, I place the seven legendary chakras, without which today's modern esoteric teachings cannot manage (again we can state that, actually, esoterics cannot be taught), and new methods of therapy are constantly being developed to treat these chakras. In my Esogetic Model, the molecule of the chakras represents information.

I consciously separate information from the term "energy", which manifests itself in the fifth molecule. At this point we have to apply the powers of visualization. In my view, information cannot exist without energy, and vice versa. Still, they are two different things.

The cybernetician Robert Wiener agrees with the biologist Frederic Vester about this new entity, information. Both attribute this third state to matter and to energy. Therefore, energy is something other than information.

Frederic Vester explains the difference between energy and information thus: "If I give energy to somebody else, then, afterwards,

I do not have it any more. However, if I give information, then I keep it and, afterwards, will still have it." This is an excellent explanation of this term.

Let us return to the fifth molecule, which I envision as the Converter System. Big ovens, or suns, inexhaustibly create the energy necessary to transfer the life-information program into the body, into the material areas of our lives. There would be no living matter, or life as we know it, without the information-energy concept. It is clear, of course, that in this dimension there is no information without energy, and vice versa. The trinity of information-energy-matter is a prerequisite for life.

A little sad and almost amused (but without arrogance) I keep track

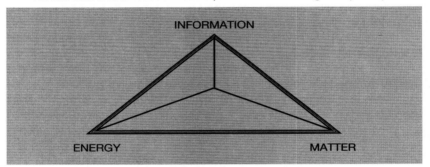

of the medical community's battle to reject an energy concept which, for example, was already taught in ancient cultures. That there are electrical currents in our bodies, is certainly undisputed. ECG and EEG are proofs of this. I cannot understand why anyone finds it so difficult to acknowledge, for example, Voll's electro-acupuncture or such follow-up methods as Vega-Test, SEG, Decoder and so forth. One almost gets the feeling that the medical community is forever obstructing itself.

I place the concept of the Formative Field in the sixth molecule. At first I thought this had something to do with the morphogenetic field postulated by Rupert Sheldrake. Today I am convinced that, in this molecule, the form-giving — or, as Dr. Franz Riedweg writes, the "formative" — has its place. Professor Heuss, one of my respected teachers, was of the opinion that the form-giving can be compared with the "primal gray" out of which light and color evolve. His explanation was that white and black stand opposite each other in a circle, and if these two entities come together and mingle, gray comes into being.

This gray mist out of which the light, the colors, the universe, the worlds and everything else has emerged, may be compared to the divine principle which we will then find again in the seventh principle, the transcendental.

Within this field thought comes into being, and then is carried, as information, by the energy of our consciousness (the "I" or waking consciousness) into the body and becomes reality.

The seventh principle, the transcendental field, as mentioned above, remains to be discussed. Transcendence comes from the Latin word, transcedere, which means to go beyond. It is the term for beyond reality and being, for going beyond the finite world, but it is also the term for absolute internalization and contemplation.

Opposite transcendence lies the term "immanence"; it clarifies the human experience, the given and the experienceable. Man's self-realization depends on transforming this striving for the transcendental into immanent goals and ideas.

In my model, this field lies in the middle of the circle. It divides the

The Opposites: White/Black - Light/Darkness

circle into an above and a below, into a right and a left. Furthermore, it is the apex of a cone which rises out of the base of the circle and its molecules. It illustrates the divine, the inexplorable, as well as the divine spark within us. This is

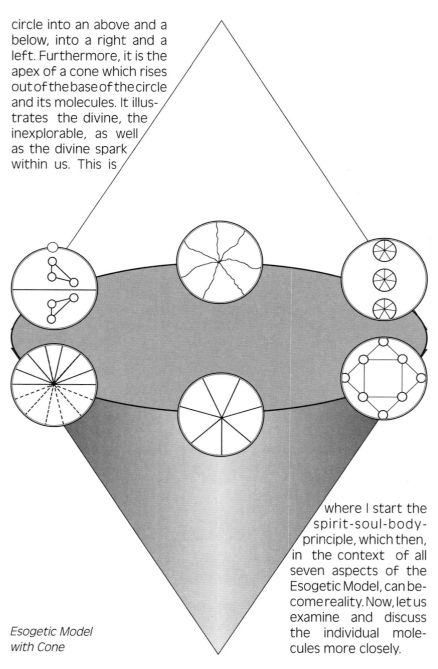

where I start the spirit-soul-body-principle, which then, in the context of all seven aspects of the Esogetic Model, can become reality. Now, let us examine and discuss the individual molecules more closely.

Esogetic Model with Cone

42

BODY SYSTEMS

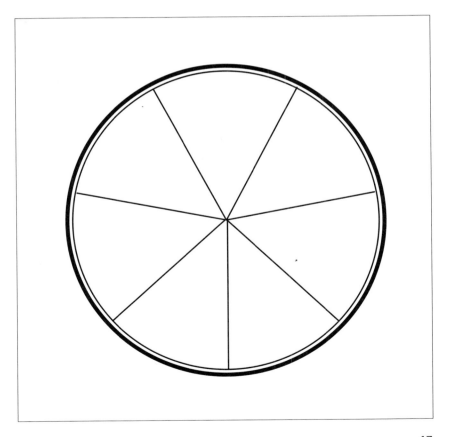

When I said earlier that the first molecule refers specifically to the material body, I was aware of the fact that, in a living organism, an exclusively material component cannot exist. The whole of life is permeated by all the informative and energetic components which comprise this dimension, our environment.

If we try to observe man's bodily reality from the material point of view alone, then we will quickly realize it is impossible. Biology, the study of the living, describes the course of development and the origin from which so many structures and forms have developed. Down to its molecules, everything is structured in indescribable variety. The uniqueness of nature's creative powers is found in its great diversity of species, the pinnacle of which is meant to be man.

The entire concept begins with the primordial act of union between sperm and egg, and the resulting blastogenesis. By this, we mean everything that follows the union of egg and sperm.

At first, after this insemination, one finds a seemingly chaotic pile of cells, which, however, rapidly and mysteriously arranges itself into order. This homogeneous, embryonic pile of cells begins to create distinctions, very exactly and precisely, in its forward development from embryo to living being. Life's entire blueprint is contained in the nucleus of the cell, in the chromosomes and genes.

Here, of course, questions arise immediately: Where does this information, this blueprint, come from? Who drew it up? Where does the overall stimulus come from? How do the cells of this chaotic pile come to know which of them is going to become a bone, a muscle, a blood, or a heart cell? A vast library seems to exist, with its coded text contained in the genes and chromosomes.

If, through this genetic code, special cells happen to evolve out of the embryonic pile and unite into organs and systems, one might believe that isolated task forces have developed, which, in their entirety, evolve into a living being. The experiment of the biologist Gordon, mentioned earlier, shows this is not the case, and that each cell, despite its special task, knows of the others. Therefore, all cells of a living organism know of each other, and in their nucleus, even though each is specialized, the entire book of life is contained. In the example of the intestine cell, the book is only open at the page named "intestine cell".

Now, if each cell knows of the others, what they do and what their functions are, long-distance intercommunication must exist. There has to be a comprehensive cell-communication system allowing a constant exchange of information. Looked at logically, it cannot work without this information exchange.

All life's needs, whatever they are, must be understood by each of life's components. Otherwise, life would not run smoothly. This requires a special communication system able to coordinate all incoming information and communicate it to the whole.

If we now want to describe such a system, we cannot avoid concerning ourselves briefly with biophysical processes. The physician Dr. Fritz-Albert Popp, a man I greatly honor and to whom I personally owe much, is particularly concerned with biocommunication. In his book *Die Biologie des Lichtes* he clearly describes the revolutionizing discovery of the ultra-faint light radiation existing in the cell.

This all began with the sensational experiment of the Russian Alexander G. Gurwitsch in the year 1922. He observed that the cells of

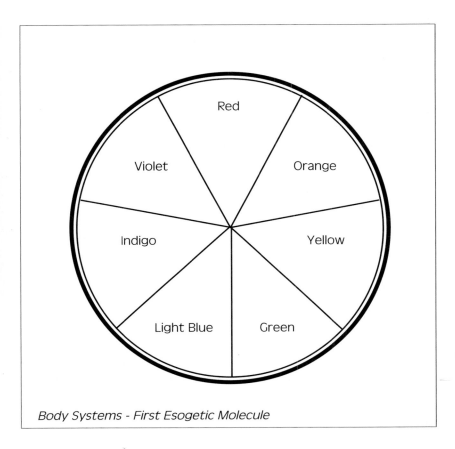

Body Systems - First Esogetic Molecule

an onion stalk are prone to increased segmentation as soon as they are approached by the roots of a second onion. In order to exclude the possibility of chemical messengers traveling from the roots of the second onion to the stalk of the first — which could stimulate segmentation — Gurwitsch shielded the two onions from each other by placing them under glass. Astonishingly, segmentation was also stimulated when glass separated the two onions.

The use of normal window glass, however, resulted in no evidence of cell activity. The "miracle" only happened with quartz glass as the medium of separation. It is well-known that ultraviolet radiation is absorbed by normal glass, but passes through quartz glass. Out of this comes the conclusion that only ultraviolet light is able to transport growth impulses.

A further experiment confirms the preceding. In this context, I quote Dr. F.A. Popp: "In two containers made of quartz glass, cells are living in a nutrient solution. The sides of the containers touch each other. One cell culture is infected with a virus. Almost simultaneously, the cells of the neighboring colony also become sick."

To begin with, this is an almost inconceivable process: information from a hermetically sealed glass invades another that is also hermetically sealed.

Today, Popp is examining the ultra-faint light radiation, which he describes as "the gentle rustle of leaves in the wind." For this, he is using the so-called photomultiplier which, according to him, is a thousand times darker than the best photographic seal and, yet, is still too light. Popp says that normal living cells emit a regular stream of photons. This means there is light in a living cell. Popp explains that this light is very faint and that it corresponds to the intensity of a candle flame observed from a distance of fifteen miles.

Photons are the atoms or quantums of light radiation. If we assume that the healthy cells of our body have a harmonious, uniform quality of light flow, then it is logical that sick cells must have a disharmonious flow of photons. From this, one can certainly conclude that, in the near future, the quality of light/photon activity will provide us with information about the nature of disease. This takes us back to the Esogetic consideration of the first molecule.

I also start with the supposition that light and photons participate in the business of communicating between our cells, organs and systems, that they must be the information carriers who rule over man's spirit-soul-body synthesis. In my view I go even further: I believe the entire spectrum of the vibrations of the universe is mirrored in the being, man. This is confirmed by the first law of Hermes Trismegistos: "As above, so below", "As on the outside, so on the inside." This means, then, that nothing exists on the inside that is not present, as well, on the outside.

Next, let us return to the light which originates in each of our cells and which can be understood as the language of the cells. Since the time of Isaac Newton, we know that light can be divided into its spectral components. If we pass white light through a prism, we will obtain the popular spectrum of colors.

This circle of colors, from red to violet, seems to have a special relationship to the "weal and woe" of bodily functions. This comes from ancient traditions who dealt with the healing force of colors.

All great cultures of the earth have used light and colors in treating their sick people. The Colorpuncture I have developed experientially proves the effectiveness of color therapy in daily practice.

I have divided the Esogetic body molecule into seven aspects, because light has seven color structures. I envision the cells, organs and systems of our bodies as vibrating within these seven color aspects. That means, for me — from the angle of the theory of colors — that in diagnosis and therapy, one should no longer focus on individual cells and organs, but, instead, consider the whole system of colors with all its associated individual aspects.

Because everything is subject to the laws of light, it may therefore be possible that, in the near future, using as yet undeveloped apparatuses, the therapist will be able to examine the quality of the biophotons and draw his diagnostic conclusions from this examination.

If a man with an experiential focus looks at the scientific research on light and biophotons in the living cell, he cannot avoid developing further hypotheses, even if, as yet, they have no validity in the high temple of science. He has a right to do so, especially if he applies his ideas and experiences on the ill in his daily practice.

So, I see the human body, in its wholeness, as a system of light and color. The whole system, this "body", is always healthy when the single vibration-quantities are in an all-encompassing equilibrium. Within the Esogetic body molecule, the colors arrange themselves from red to violet, according to their valence.

Even though the body and its smallest aspects, the cells, possess the entire information of life, and even though we can assume that everything can be found in everything, the being, man, still needs coordination.

For the moment, let us assume that the body of man is like a

marionette. A marionette's nature is to require a puppeteer with the skill to move it in the appropriate way. As everywhere in life, there are good and bad actors, and the marionette will only move according to how the puppeteer manipulates it. A bad puppeteer will create disharmony in the performance, and this means that, in reference to our lives, with inadequate coordination (a bad puppeteer), the cells and organs must necessarily follow the bad performance.

In our lives the puppeteer is sitting in our brain. He has a certain principal position, even though we know, of course, that he is not directing the play. We also know he has neither created the marionette nor written the script, nor did he have the idea in the first place. Even so, the performance cannot take place without him.

In the Esogetic Model, therefore, coordination occupies second place. In my opinion, the second Esogetic molecule includes the sevenfold coordination of one's life.

COORDINATION ORGANS

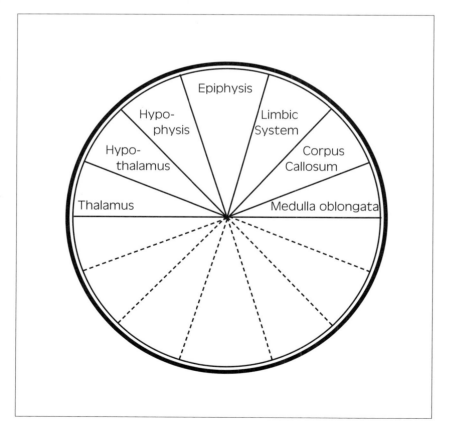

As I stated earlier, the seven coordination organs, as I see them, by no means explain the functions of our brain. However, if one wants to delve into the enigma of life, then insights into these functionings are sufficient. These insights are the aspects of our brains we are going to discuss here.

I am of the opinion these seven coordination organs occupy a certain key position. This is very important to me, because, on the one hand, certain points and zones on our body for these organs have been known for some time. On the other hand, I have discovered more, rounding out the system. These points or zones represent a "hot line" to headquarters.

By simple manipulation, the function of these areas can be illus-

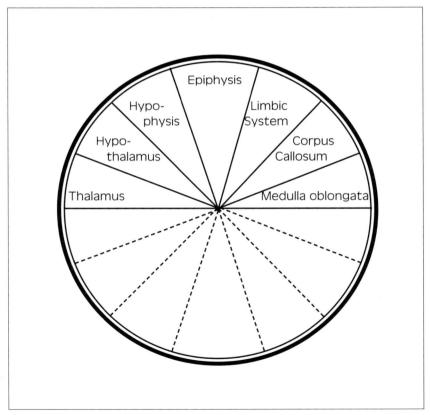

Coordination Organs (Council of Seven) - Second Esogetic Molecule

trated, as well as their connection to a person's complaints and pains. I will refer to this later and invite the reader to try it.

First, let us take a look at the well-known functions of the individual organs as described in literature. I start the list with the Thalamus or Mount of Seeing and, following, describe the Hypothalamus, Hypophysis, Epiphysis, the Midbrain or Limbic System, the Bridge between the Hemispheres or Corpus Callosum and, finally, the switching station between higher and lower, the Medulla Oblongata.

I. The Mount of Seeing (Thalamus opticus)

The Thalamus serves as a switchboard. It occupies the largest portion of gray mass in the midbrain. It has corresponding fiber systems which are connected with other parts of the central nervous system: the cerebral cortex, the extra-pyramidal system, the cerebellum and the spinal cord. It is the switchboard for optic and acoustic lines. It is considered to be the "gate to consciousness", because it switches sensitive and sensory stimuli from the outer and inner worlds to the cerebral cortex.

The Thalamus is one of the most important independent coordination organs, connecting feelings of touch, pain and temperature with taste, balance and the sensations of the inner organs. In this synthesis, emphatic emotional reactions are produced, such as liking or disliking.

Because of its connection to the extra-pyramidal system, the Thalamus plays a role in the occurrence of movements of expression and psycho-reflexes, which we then recognize as kinetic reactions. Expressions of pain, or "fight or flight" reflexes, are typical examples of such kinetic reactions.

In summary, we can state that the following fall within the responsibility of the Thalamus opticus:

a) surface sensibility;

b) channels of hearing and seeing;

c) the process of becoming conscious;

d) sensory feedback.

Now we turn our attention to the Hypothalamus-Hypophysis system.

2. Hypothalamus

In the release of hormones directly into the blood, this organ is considered the highest authority. This is the endocrine function.

The Hypothalamus is situated in the lower part of the midbrain and is the pre-eminent coordination organ for all endocrine glands. The neural information it creates (afferences) influences the endocrine glands through vegetative nerves. The hormonal information (efferences) controls the endocrine glands of the lower orders through the Hypothalamus-Hypophysis system. Therefore, the Hypothalamus is the center of coordination for the organism's entire vegetative and endocrine processes. It the most important organ for the regulation of the body's inner milieu.

The Hypothalamus has close connections to the Limbic system and, via the Thalamus, to the cerebral cortex. The hormonal distribution not only plays a part in vegetative functions, such as energy and water supply, and circulation and breathing, but is also connected with sleeping and waking rhythms, and with psychological and emotional factors. For example, if women fail to menstruate in situations of stress, a control fault in the Hypothalamus can be the cause.

3. Hypophysis

The Hypophysis, or pituitary gland, is considered the switchboard of the endocrine system. It is bean-shaped, weighs 0.6 grams, and is centrally located at the base of the skull.

The Hypophysis consists of two parts: the glandular part (Adenohypophysis) and the cerebral part (Neurohypophysis). The frontal lobe of the pituitary is divided into prehypophysis, mid-lobe and funnel-lobe.

The release of hormones from the pituitary's frontal lobe is direct-

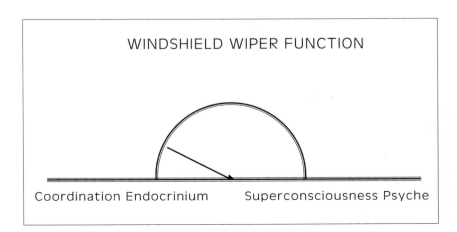

WINDSHIELD WIPER FUNCTION

Coordination Endocrinium   Superconsciousness Psyche

ed by higher-echelon hormones from the Hypothalamus. In most cases, a hormonal discharge is preceded by a nerve stimulus in the central nervous system. The nerve-hormone switchboard is primarily the Hypothalamus. It translates the nerve stimulus into a hormone release from the front and back lobes of the pituitary.

In summary, the Hypophysis is the switchboard of the endocrine system and, therefore, the most important organ for the hormonal-vegetative system. The information exchange with inner organic and inner secretion mechanisms travels via the Hypophysis. It has a direct connection with the Hypothalamus and the Thalamus. In addition, it can be regarded as an essential switchboard for all emotions.

My observations have confirmed my opinion that, in our lives, the hormonal inner-secretion processes and the psyche form an indivisible unity I call the "windshield wiper function."

This term aptly describes what I observe again and again in my daily practice with the ill. Just think of the hormonal processes of puberty or menopause, and the often strong psychological stress that is involved, and the correlation becomes clear. Furthermore, if we remind ourselves that no emotional reaction takes place in our lives without prior hormonal processes, then the term "windshield wiper function" becomes even clearer. Viewed in this context, permanent psychological stress is always connected to the Hypothalamus-Hypophysis system.

4. Epiphysis (Pineal Gland)
Not much can be found in literature about this gland, although it is, in my opinion, a most important organ. In the 17th century, the French philosopher Descartes conjectured that the Epiphysis could be the residence of the soul.

Throughout the ages, the pineal gland has been envisioned as the gland of light. In esoterics, it has been associated with the seventh and supreme chakra. This chakra sits at the highest point of our heads. The stem of the flowering chakra reaches deep into our brain, into the pineal gland.

In traditional Chinese medicine, one of the channels in which life-energy flows, the internal channel of the liver meridian, ends precisely in the center of the skull. This is the area where the seventh chakra is situated, and where the connection to the Epiphysis is thought to be located. This is interesting because, through the hormone melatonin which it creates, the pineal gland is connected with the liver. Of late, this hormone has been considered to contribute to the rise of depression. It is a proven fact that too much melatonin leads to extreme fatigue, and too little, to insomnia. In cooperation with the Hypophysis, the hormone melatonin regulates the process known as prolactin synthesis. It is also interesting that the Epiphysis can hinder the creation of sex hormones in adolescence and, as a result, delay the beginning of puberty. It has therefore been called "the gland of innocence and chastity."

The pineal gland is also said to be the central coordination organ of our "inner clock". Everyone knows it is possible, just by one's inner attitude, to wake up in the morning without an alarm clock or a wake-up service. Anyone can try it. It just needs a bit of practice.

In the evening, before going to bed, simply picture a large clock, maybe a railway station clock. Now, imagine turning the hands of the clock to the time you would like to awaken in the morning. Hold this image for a time, and allow the visualized clock to become bigger and bigger. Then you can fall asleep confidently, because you will wake up on time the next morning. This inner wake-up service functions independently of winter or summer time zones.

The pineal gland certainly has many more functions which still remain to be discovered.

In medicine, the pineal gland is also called Corpus pineale because its shape resembles a pineal cone. It is 1.2 cm in length, weighs approximately 170 mg, and is situated in the roof of the third cerebral ventricle. It is connected with the brain through stems. It has been shown in animals that the pineal gland seems to play an important part in coordinating the hormonal processes of the Hypothalamus-Hypophysis system.

5. The Midbrain (Limbic system)
Anatomically, our brain consists of three parts. Stacked, so to speak, one on top of the other, they comprise the entire human brain. Professor Paul McLean classifies these in terms of evolution, as follows:

a) the reptile brain;

b) the midbrain or Limbic system;

c) the new brain or the human cerebrum.

Similarly, C.G. Jung reflected on this three-fold brain and postulated that not only does man have a personal unconscious, but also a superpersonal unconscious. He points out that each human being possesses some primary knowledge which is the result of the most important experiences of mankind as a whole. If this primary knowledge equates to the memory of the origin of time, then we, as human beings, may have something like a memory of creation.

The thesis of Professor Rupert Sheldrake is even more thrilling. He believes the experiences of all living beings, throughout time, are recorded in huge databases he calls morphogenetic fields. This means all human beings of the present are connected to these fields. He believes this is the only way living beings can pass on new abilities or qualities to other living beings anywhere in the world. The hypothesis of the morphogenetic fields, which can be compared with a huge mental computer, is fantastic. At present, experiments are being done to transfer knowledge or abilities across long distances without the use of any media such as language or pictures.

The model of the brain function presented by the Israeli researcher Professor P.S. Rothschild is nonetheless fantastic. He sees our brain as having five layers. Here we can see the connection with Professor McLean, who speaks of three layers.

The top layer corresponds to the human brain. Underneath is the layer of the mammal brain. Emotions are its special expression.

The next layer below is the reptile brain. Here we find the brain of habits, but also the memory of times long past, of all the millions of years of evolution towards present-day man.

The last two layers are associated with the vertebrates and the invertebrates.

According to him, the upper layers rule over the lower; however, the lower layers must find a means of release when the pressure within the hierarchy becomes too strong. This happens through dream pictures, which ascend into the upper layers of consciousness as primary pictures, or as Jung calls them, archetypal pictures.

During the course of this book, I will suggest to the reader how to stimulate his own dreaming, and how to come into contact with the deeper levels of his consciousness via some zones and points I have discovered. It may sound unbelievable, but my careful observations of innumerable ill people have convinced me that everything that is, is recorded on the outer covering of our bodies, on the skin. We simply have to find the appropriate keys to unlock the doors of our unconscious and open up paths into the depths of our beings.

Now let us return to the three-fold brain of Paul McLean, especially to the Limbic system which, for me, occupies such an important role within the coordination hierarchy. Again, let us start from the ancient or reptile brain. It consists of the extended spinal cord, the bridge and the ascending reticular system of the metencephalon. Here we find the center for the "fight or flight" reaction and the mechanisms of relaxation. From here, a great number of physical and psychological needs are regulated, such as breathing, circulation, blood pressure, sensations of pain, and sleep patterns.

R.L. Johnson says, "We have to learn methods to reduce stress; otherwise, the ancient brain programs us to react to each situation in our lives with aggression or flight." Later, Johnson states that if man constricts himself to these inflexible, well-worn patterns of behavior that correspond to the reptile brain, it will result in his living in a tight-fitting armor which will hinder him from reaching further levels of development. In other words, he will remain anchored to his habits.

Within the coordination hierarchy, my particular issue is the midbrain. It belongs to those parts of our overall organism in which the blood circulates most. On the one hand, it regulates biochemical functions, such as blood sugar level; on the other, waking and sleeping patterns, food and water intake, heart frequency, blood pressure, sexuality and, most importantly, the release of hormones.

The Limbic system is the most important connection between body and emotions. Emotional reactions like joy, anger, rage, pain, hunger, thirst, tension and relaxation are all situated here. Furthermore, will power, a major part of our memory, and the ability to love are anchored in the Limbic system. All unexplainable fears and phobias seem to thrust themselves into our consciousness from here, exerting their destructive influences on our lives.

Most important, it seems to me, in the context of the seven coordination aspects of Esogetics, is to focus on regulating the Limbic system. The newly-discovered coordination-therapy possibilities, especially the zones and points of the Limbic system, can offer help in this respect.

It is well known that the midbrain contributes to all learning processes; therefore, it is necessary to consider it in treating children and adults with learning difficulties. My observations of dyslexic children and, especially, my successes in administering new Limbic system therapies, prove again and again that regulating the emotional spheres of life is of particular importance.

Once again, let me repeat: in the midbrain the emotions have their home. Here, the choice of our spontaneous conduct seems to be made. Since the release of hormones is also regulated in the midbrain, it seems reasonable to assume that there cannot be any conscious emotional reactions or feelings without hormones. This would also mean that our waking consciousness and our rational reactions are secondary.

Before man becomes conscious of something, before he performs any mental activity, the impulse has already been processed in the deeper layers of his brain. Therefore man should become more humble and, as Johnson suggests, try to synchronize the three aspects of his brain. Man should set aside some of the rational structures of which he is so proud, and whose dominance he is usually striving for, in order to give more space to perception, premonition and faith; in short, to the intuitive and the inspirational. This can only be achieved by synchronizing the three parts of the brain.

At present, there are a variety of relaxation techniques which can be used with success. It does not matter whether one meditates or relaxes through self-hypnosis or apparatuses, so long as it serves to install an "escalator" in the layers of our brain. The important thing is to come into contact with one's total being, according to the spirit-soul-body principle.

Esogetic therapies offer a simple means of achieving this. At first glance, they often seem unbelievable; however, when practiced, they fulfill the expected. In this context, the Color-Sound therapies and the new Esogetic Sound Patterns, based upon the frequencies of the Esogetic Model, should be given special attention. Later, I will go into this in more detail.

In summary, we can say that the Limbic system belongs to particularly important areas of our lives and, therefore, occupies a special place within the coordination system.

What remains to be discussed is the new brain, with which, on this earth, only man is endowed.

The cerebrum divides itself into right and left sides or hemispheres. Extensive nerve connections link the ancient brain, the midbrain and the cerebrum closely together. Most of these connecting paths lead from the Limbic system to the right hemisphere of the cerebrum. This is also an indication of the importance of the middle part of our brain.

One attributes special creative qualities to the right half of the cerebrum. Whenever we have access to the right half of the brain, our life becomes creative. Intuition and inspiration also seem to have their home here. It happens often that, in a flash, one is struck by a thought or an idea, or a sudden realization seizes one's consciousness, then one just knows, "This is right; this is simply so."

The left hemisphere is regarded as the seat of all rational, intellectual, mathematical and analytical thinking. The ability to speak and write originates here, as well as the capacity to coordinate and inte- grate the functions of all other areas of the brain. The left hemi- sphere brings everything we are into order and balance.

If we succeed in joining the two sides of the cerebrum together, we will be capable of endless creative performance. Johnson suggests in his book *Ich schreibe mir die Seele frei* (I free my soul by writing), the creativity of writing a diary to attain this goal. There are certainly in- numerable other possibilities to reach the same objective; we simply need to stand up and set out on the path. We have to take the first step to experience the miracle of who we really are.

We have now reached to the sixth principle of the Esogetic coor- dination molecule, the demarcation line between the two halves of the cerebrum: the Bridge between the Hemispheres or the Corpus callo- sum.

6. Bridge between the Hemispheres (Corpus callosum)

Here we find strong nerve fiber connections running across and connecting the two sides of the cerebrum. The bridge of the Corpus callosum consists of stem, tuberosity and knee. This bridge separates emotions and rationality, and also separates the cerebrum from the stem brain. This results in a functional cross dividing left and right, as well as above and below. The midbrain, on the other hand, has connec- tions to the cerebrum as well as to the stem brain.

The information contained in this functional cross was revealed to me by disorders known as laterality disturbances. These laterality dis- turbances become visible through the Energy Emission Analysis (EEA) I developed, a diagnosis made using Kirlian photography. I will elaborate on this diagnostic method later.

A laterality disturbance is a right-left disorder of the hemispheres of the cerebrum. I know, today, that it is impossible to regulate or ad- just any kind of disease without first removing such a blockage.

One statistic that emerged from studies in my institute proves that, in most cases, laterality disturbances appear before the end of puberty. If we find such a disturbance coming from the right side of the brain, it is caused by a physical trauma. A similar disturbance coming from the left side indicates an emotional trauma, such as a shock or other experience of psychological stress in childhood. The rea- son for this remains a mystery. Only considering the entire Esogetic Model, especially the third molecule, can help solve this puzzle.

Let us summarize again the most important functions of the Corpus callosum: separation of the right and left hemispheres of the brain and, therefore, of emotions and rationality; and separation of the cerebrum and stem brain from each other.

Now, only the seventh of the coordination organs I have selected remains to be discussed, the Medulla oblongata.

7. Medulla oblongata

The Medulla oblongata represents the lower part of the rhomb-encephalon. Starting approximately at the height of the first cervical segment, it stretches forward to the lower rim of the Corpus callosum and backwards to the middle of the rhombic pit. It contains such vital systems as the breath center, the heart-circulation center, and the center for vomiting. I observed that this part of the brain must have a direct connection to the solar plexus.

By simply applying pressure on a zone at the back of the head, it is possible to remove any tension or pain caused by stress or fear and felt in the area of the stomach. This zone at the back of the head belongs to the reflex area of the Medulla oblongata. Moreover, this area has connections to the midbrain and the stem brain, and, therefore, to the coordination organs described earlier.

I understand the Medulla oblongata to be the switching station for information coming from the brain (efferences) and the sensory feedback coming from below.

The Medulla oblongata is one of the most important topographic areas in Kirlian (EEA) diagnosis. Again and again, one can observe that, in the case of such systemic diseases as multiple sclerosis, Parkinson's disease and other serious disorders, especially strong phenomena overload this sector. But the Medulla oblongata sector also reveals strain in the case of clinically healthy people with severe complaints of numbness in their hands and feet, or coldness or heaviness in their extremities. My Esogetic thought model offers simple manipulations for these situations, and I teach these in my seminars.

I see a further connection of the Medulla oblongata to focal intoxication of the head. This is a lymphatic irritation in the areas of the teeth, the sinuses of the skull, the upper and lower jaw, the ears, and the downward-draining lymph. If one draws a horizontal line from the area of the Medulla oblongata towards the front of the head, one reaches the area where focal intoxications occur. One can no longer really doubt this realization. Everyone has most likely heard that a tooth abscess can trigger sciatic pain or migraine.

Unfortunately, the whole lymph system plays a relatively unimportant role in official medicine. In comparison, natural healing sciences place this system in the foreground of their diagnostic considerations. The lymph system, in connection with the area of the Medulla oblongata, could play a part in the development of the dread systemic diseases. One dares to make this statement because systemic diseases belong to that seventy percent of all diseases whose root causes are still in the dark.

Therefore, the area of the Medulla oblongata became one of the

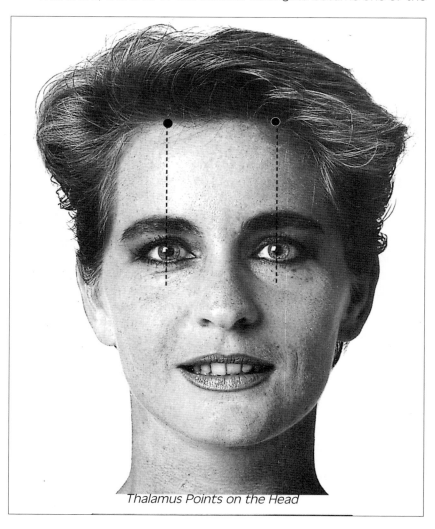

Thalamus Points on the Head

most important areas of coordination in my daily practice. I was able to develop a large number of specific methods of treatment which signal hope. However, we are still far away from being able to provide the absolute healing impulse to seriously sick people.

In the chapter on the second Esogetic molecule, I have tried to provide the reader with a brief overview of the functions of our brain in general, and of the coordination organs I consider most important. At the end of this chapter I want to invite the reader to experiment him-

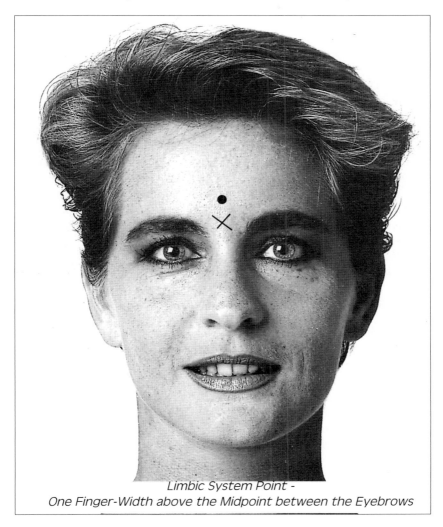

Limbic System Point -
One Finger-Width above the Midpoint between the Eyebrows

self. I will choose a few methods from the wide range of coordination therapies. These therapies are so simple and effective that one can try them on oneself at any time without fear of any unpleasant reaction. The manipulations are simple and easy to carry out.

Let us return to the beginning of this chapter, to the first coordination organ, the Mount of Seeing or Thalamus opticus. As mentioned earlier, it represents consciousness and is, so to speak, the door to consciousness.

At this point, I wish to state that any ordinary pain, such as lower back pain, headache, stomach or rheumatic pain, has to do with just this consciousness. If the points assigned to the Thalamus are treated in the way I describe later, the pain disappears. It goes without saying that, in the case of strongly degenerative diseases, pain cannot be removed in seconds. Therefore, at first, we will confine ourselves to less serious complaints.

The therapeutic points of the Thalamus can be found on the forehead. If we draw lines on the forehead directly upwards from the exact middle of each eye, we will find the points of the Thalamus at the hairline, or where it should be. With a blunt tool, like the back of a pencil, we can palpate this area and identify the two most painful points. Now we test on both sides for the point that is the more painful, and massage this point for about ten seconds. In most cases, complaints dissolve immediately, and for a certain length of time, no matter where they were located in the body.

With some people, I have seen this simple manipulation bring about a lasting release from pain. They report that, without knowing exactly why, their lives have changed.

It may be possible that irregularities in a person's consciousness, irregularities of which he himself is not aware, can lead to a blockage, in the course of which deeper and deeper layers of his being become involved until, finally, they express themselves with the signal: "Pain!" We will see, later, that the body's bone system, for example, has a specific relationship to the totality of our lives.

We close this chapter with a second example. Many people suffer from extreme fatigue, especially in the morning. They accept it because they have been told they may have circulation problems or low blood pressure, or, simply, that they are grumpy in the morning.

As described above, circulation is related to the Limbic system. There are three predominant points in the Limbic system. Usually, one of them is enough to regularize fatigue and exhaustion. This often requires the suggested manipulation be carried out a few days in a row.

The point mentioned can be found about one finger-width above the middle of the eyebrows. First, locate it with the head of a pencil, and then, in a clockwise direction, massage it firmly, but without hurting yourself, for about one minute. Already, after a minute, you will feel that something is happening, that something has changed. This manipulation can be repeated several times a day and, if needed, several days in a row. Those who already practice my Colorpuncture at home with the Perlux set should radiate this point for one minute with the color orange.

Just try these simple self-treatments; then you will be convinced of the impact these coordination organs have on our lives. During the course of this book, I will illustrate further simple possibilities that may convince you of my statements.

At this point, I would like to close the chapter on the Esogetic molecule of coordination and open a discussion on the third aspect of Esogetic thinking. On the one hand, this third aspect comprises a totally new form of therapy; on the other, I believe I have found, here, a connecting link in the body-brain coordination unit. This area is absolutely new and required many years of patient observation to explore it and to work it out. What I am setting down and describing, here and now, has been experientially verified through my own research and experimentation. This explains why there is no other literature on this theme.

Daily, and with great success, many therapists all over the world use this new method of therapy via the Transmitter Relays. This system is so extensive that the therapist requires a great deal of theoretical knowledge and practical training to be able to apply this method in his daily work. I will therefore confine myself in the next chapter to a brief insight into this — as I believe it to be — miracle of creation.

First, however, I wish to offer a short introduction into the methods I have developed. This is meant to contribute to a better understanding of the chapter on the Transmitter Relays. I begin with the year 1973, the year the foundation for all my present findings was laid.

ENERGY EMISSION ANALYSIS (EEA)

In 1973, I began experimenting with Kirlian photography. At that time, my brother Eberhard Mandel helped me with the technical actualization of my ideas. Diagnosis through Kirlian-effect emissions — my already widespread Energy Emission Analysis (EEA) method — came into being.

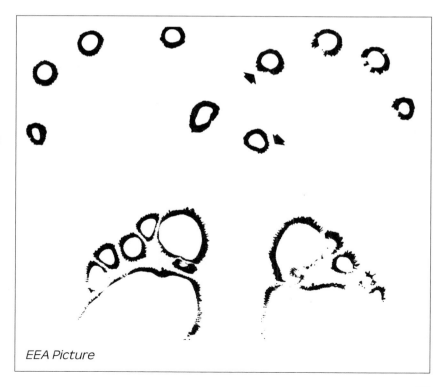

EEA Picture

TOPOGRAPHY
ENERGY EMISSION ANALYSIS

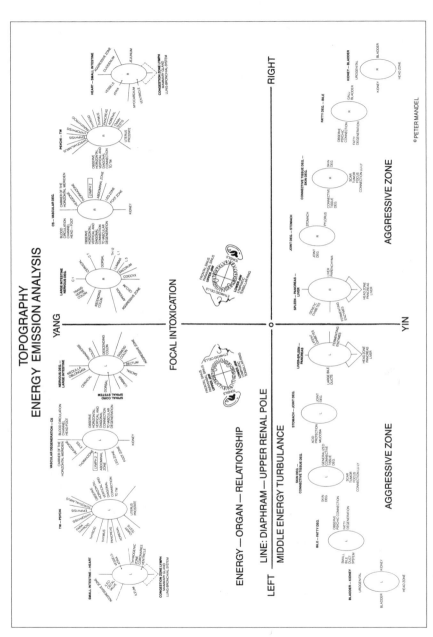

© PETER MANDEL

TOPOGRAPHY EEA

In those days, the idea was still dominant that radiations appearing on photographic paper represented man's legendary aura. I believe I have contributed to demystifying these conceptions. Work with and on EEA is far from complete; however, in terms of each individual, whose emission is just as unique as his thumbprint, increasingly subtle insights can be obtained and described. Diagnostic indications result from the observation of twenty small areolas of radiation, appearing like black and white suns on the photographic paper.

In my opinion, the color emissions other people consider to be of special importance are of limited diagnostic value. One reason is that the color of the visible areolas depends on technical factors and is not, as frequently thought, an expression of the photographed energies of the body. This depends on the coating of the individual photographic materials and also on the quality of the gas used in the production apparatus between high frequency electronics and dielectrics. Therefore, I decided in favor of black and white photography, which is able to show me all the individual's imprints and, frankly, provokes me to holistic thinking.

To interpret the visible phenomena logically, one must comprehend that, in explaining the connections and reactions shown in such a

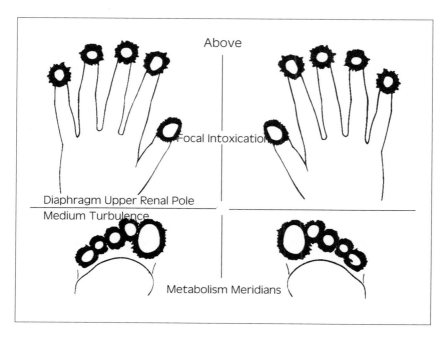

69

picture, polar thinking is a prerequisite.

It became apparent there are only three main groupings of phenomena, but these, in themselves, allow for a wide range of variations. This alone, however, would never have allowed adequate diagnosis and analysis.

Through observing certain laws in the emission phenomena, I formulated a system of interpretation. First of all, I developed a topography which located virtually all organs and systems. After that, the law of directional energy flow, as revealed in the EEA picture, followed. The polar connections — above-below and right-left, as well as right hand-left foot and vice versa — showed, again and again, the regularity to which all EEA-picture emissions are subject.

Three important considerations must be take into account when interpreting energetic phenomena:

a) interpretation of the organ sector;
b) meaning of the phenomena appearing in that sector;
c) connections of the organ sectors and phenomena
   in relation to directional energy flow.

Any criticism of doctors and scientists can easily be invalidated by a closer look at the basic principles I have established, and which confer the same validity on EEA as on any other earnest method. The objection is undoubtedly correct that the impulse velocity of man's energy is so high that, when taking serial pictures, the entire emission will change again and again. If this were the only relevant factor my EEA would be worthless. But it is exactly this that is of no great importance. As mentioned above, it is the organ sector, with its connections, that has top priority.

The quantities of emission, or the individual phenomena, are simply the expression of the momentary situation of that sector. They can either present themselves as insufficient, toxic-aggressive or degenerative, and this can then be applied to the overall situation and to the person as a whole. This is the only way to obtain exact information on the present condition of a person, his symptoms and irregularities.

My EEA has supplied the basis for the findings of today's Esogetics because each emission contains everything the Esogetic Model has to offer, including not only theoretical but also practical principles of application. The emissions allow an interpretation of all the connections between subtle and gross matter. In this way, EEA is a method which turns one's "unrealities" inside out and makes them visible; and when something becomes visible, we can recognize and interpret it. Reproducible and recurring states can be described. All of these are important steps in explaining the Esogetic Model and its seven aspects.

This ability to explain existing states of illness opened up the possibility of translating the information and phenomena into appropriate therapy models. Since 1973 I have succeeded in developing more than two hundred new therapies. On the one hand, I have given new interpretation and definition to known and existing conclusions; on the other, I have discovered totally new zones with astounding connections to the visible phenomena.

With this, the new, and above all crucial question of energetic regulation arose, independent of the medical description of the individual disease. This allowed me to draw conclusions which were logical and conclusive; for if it is possible to make invisible energies visible and to deduce indications of symptoms and irregularities from this, then these signs and phenomena must, at the same time, contain the key for reversal, for erasing negative information.

Since it became possible to deduce the cause of a disease from the energy-information signs of an EEA, any therapeutic method had to fulfill the basic condition of having a regulating effect on the informative-energetic system. Treatment with light and, especially, with colors — practiced by many cultures on this earth for thousands of years — attracted my attention.

Already, in 1975, I began thinking about how to make it easy for people to relate color therapy to the EEA, and to apply it. Many experiments followed. Finally, in 1978, my Colorpuncture was born. Over the years I developed it further, refining it until it attained the outstanding extent, recognition and significance we observe today.

Now I had two methods: the diagnostic-analytical EEA and the energy-regulating Colorpuncture. Both methods are of an informative-energetic nature.

I would like to emphasize again that, previously, I had already experimented with the possibilities of energy movement within the meridians. Acu-Impulse therapy (acupuncture with piezoelectric impulses) preceded color therapy and brought valuable insights into directional energy flows in our bodies. The difference between piezoelectric impulses and color vibration is that Acu-Impulse gives a push to the energy in the direction of the flow, flushing out possible energy blockages. Energy flow, an essential condition for a pain-free life, becomes harmonized.

Contrary to this, Colorpuncture has a different approach. It assumes that light and color are, in themselves, already information — information whose primordial character is contained in every living thing.

It is contained as that indestructible, unknown factor in the rhythm of life to which everything is subject, and which is indispensable for the existence of life.

Whenever light falls on our skin, or whenever we take in colors through our eyes or our skin, resonating processes are set in motion which can balance out existing irregularities. If applied early enough — that is, in times of health — Colorpuncture is unsurpassed in its preventative effects.

The assumption that not only color frequencies but also acoustic frequencies could have harmonizing effects on the human organism presented a new challenge. In my view, in harmonizing life-processes, these sound frequencies — which came out of the exact conversion of the point combinations of Colorpuncture as they are successfully used in my practice — should bring the same results. My idea was that these sound frequencies, in respect to harmonizing life-processes, must bring the same result as colors. By now, this has been confirmed thousands of times.

What is still amazing is the fact that the point combinations, if applied in logical order, produce a harmonious tonal sequence when converted into sounds. Thanks to the musical knowledge, skills and intuition of Kay Korten and Ludovika Helm, completely new techniques were able to be developed, breathing life and consequence into the model I had projected.

A next step in the interpretation of the Esogetic Model was, as stated earlier, the discovery of the Transmitter Relays and the theory of the Energy Converters. Both of them, in their own right, have their own laws and are arranged in logical order. They should be viewed hierarchically, from bottom to top.

More recently, in relation to the known rhythms of beta-alpha-theta-delta as described in neurology, I am researching as yet unknown processes concerning man's brain waves. It became possible to explore a new field as the strong affinity of our brain waves to diseases, psychological irregularities, stress and so on, grew more and more apparent. I am not talking about pathological-neurological alterations like, for example, epileptiform syndromes; rather, I am speak-ing of such day-to-day complaints as painful joints, increased fat valence in the blood or the bed-wetting of children. It seems the informative-energetic signals of the Esogetic Model bring about more and more refined possibilities for regulation.

This does not exhaust, much less explain, the whole range of discoveries. That would go beyond the scope of this book. However, the

Esogetic thinking which attempts to make inexplicable processes grasp-able is inherent in all of my therapeutic methods. All of my discoveries and developments have an esoteric and energetic character; in this syn-thesis, therefore, we are dealing with "Esogetic" phenomena.

A short overview on Colorpuncture and Color-Sound therapy fol-lows. This is necessary for an understanding of the following Esogetic molecules. It is not only important to clarify the status of each mole-cule within the model, but also to develop ways and means of thinking.

I am well aware that I cannot simply transfer everything I think or do to the whole of mankind and to its manner of thinking. Still, I be-lieve Esogetics is an offer for people who think differently to come to grips with the new possibilities it contains. Furthermore, I believe the present time needs Esogetics, just as in the past different views and thought models were needed for men to ponder what needed ponder-ing in those days. So, perhaps, Esogetic thinking can initiate a syn-thesis of subtle and gross realizations.

INTRODUCTION TO COLORPUNCTURE

Light and Colors Heal!

A large part of the healing systems of ancient cultures was based on this realization. One is reminded of the sun cult, where the sun was the embodiment of the divine. In order to recover with the help of the supernatural, the ill were exposed to the sun. The Egyptians, Greeks, Romans, Hindus and Chinese all knew about the healing effects of color, and developed their own methods of light and color therapy. Today there are theories that these therapies, especially those of ancient Egypt, were so advanced we can hardly imagine the level of their sophistication.

Modern light and color therapy is inseparably linked with the names of Rollier and, particularly, Finsen, who was awarded the Nobel Prize for Medicine in 1903 for his research in this area. Both worked to establish the foundation for modern medical color light therapy.

Ordinarily, practical application is confined to radiation with red and blue light, familiar in many medical practices.

Now, what is it about light and color that has a healing effect? To answer this question, let us return to the work of two important men.

In former times, it was inexplicable to man why leaves are green, why blossoms are blue, yellow or red, or why clouds are white. Isaac Newton provided the scientific explanation in the 17th century when he refracted the rays of white light with the help of a prism, thereby making visible the spectrum of colors contained in light. It was discovered that each color of the spectrum has a different vibration or wavelength. The coloring of a thing is therefore caused by the fact that its molecular structure allows certain wavelengths to pass through, while others are reflected. It is this reflected part of white light that we perceive as color.

It was Goethe who defined the physiological aspects of color as sensations of the eye. He formulated a theory of color which is still of interest today. He regarded this theory as his life's work, valuing it above his literary achievements. Despite the fact there are many other theories of color, they can all, on close inspection, be traced back to Goethe's ideas.

Contrary to Newton, Goethe did not explore the scientific aspect of colors. Rather, he researched their order, their laws of harmony, and evaluated them from the point of view of wholeness.

He discovered that the three primary colors, red, yellow and blue, are the basis of all colors, and that all other colors can be created by mixing these three. He placed these three primary colors at the corners of an equilateral triangle, an harmonious geometric figure corresponding, if transposed to another level, to the triad in music. A mixture of equal parts of two of these primary colors will yield a compound color of the first order:

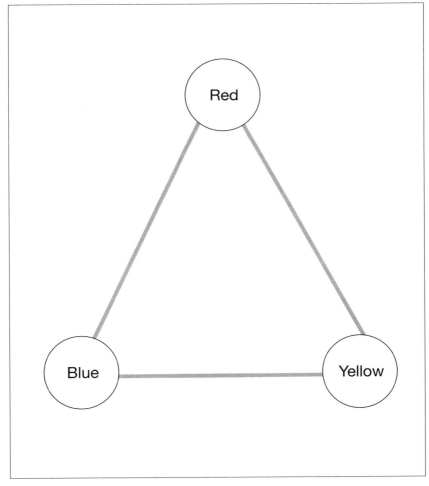

Cornerstones of Color Harmony : The Primary Colors

red and yellow make orange;
yellow and blue make green;
blue and red make violet.

If these mixed colors are placed at points between those of the primary colors from which they originate, the result will be a second equilateral triangle with its apex pointing downwards, thereby forming the six-fold color circle. The colors opposing each other in this circle are

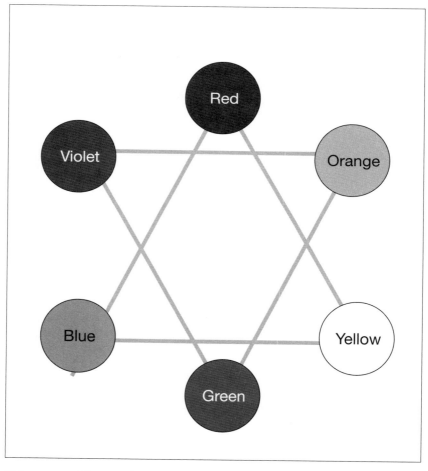

Primary and Composite Colors of the First Order from Goethe's Six-Fold Circle of Color

called complementary colors. For example, green is the complementary color of red, and vice versa. Yellow and violet are complementary to each other, just as are blue and orange.

If equal parts of complementary colors are mixed together, the result will always be gray, because, in this way, the three primary colors are again brought together. The complementary color violet, for example, consists of the two primary colors red and blue. If the com-

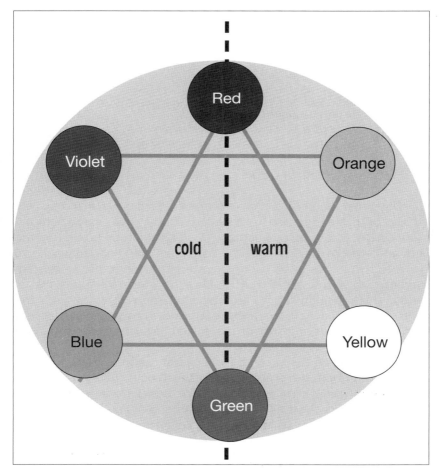

Goethe's Division of Colors into Warm and Cold

plementary color yellow is added, the three primary colors are thereby united into gray.

Each color provokes a different sensation in man. Some are perceived as warm; others, as cold. If the circle of colors is divided in half by a vertical line from red to green, the warm colors are found on the right and the cold colors on the left.

In this context, I would like to mention the work of the anatomist Becher whose findings, in 1954, demonstrated that there is a direct connection between the vegetative system and the eye. The vegetative system, the endocrine system and the psyche are directly related to each other. Because the vegetative system is related to all the organs, it can be understood that color vibrations perceived by the eye will also have an effect on the organs. This recalls Goethe's frequently-quoted lines:

Were not the eye to sun akin
The sun we never could behold.
Filled not a God's strength us within
How could the Divine hold us enthralled?

Energetic Effects of Colors

The latest biophysical research also confirms that man not only consists of matter, but also has an "energy body". This energy body actually consists, to a certain degree, of visible light, as proved by the German physicist Dr. F. A. Popp a few years ago. Popp managed to prove that the cells of all living beings emit "biophotons" or electromagnetic vibrations. Apart from visible light, these are mainly microwaves. This radiation which, according to Popp, "breathes like the gentle rustle of leaves in the wind," represents a regulating energy field that encompasses the entire organism and has an essential influence on all its biochemical processes.

The biophoton field is on a higher level than the material body. According to Popp, the effects of any substances that can influence the human organism for good or ill, travel through this energy body. This is true for medicine as well as for any food or environmental substance that can affect us in even the most minute quantities. The information they transmit affects us as electromagnetic vibrations of various frequencies.

In terms of physics, an harmonious oscillation is a regular back-and-forth movement between certain limits. The rate of oscillation within a certain period is called frequency. It is specific frequencies and, therefore, energies which influence our life functions.

Ancient traditional Chinese medicine also talks in terms of energies. For them, man is the connecting link between heaven and earth. Chinese philosophers attribute the intrinsic state of balance in man to a universal force or life energy, called *chi*. This *chi* manifests itself as yin and yang, which, in the human body, simultaneously work together yet are antagonists. The bipolarity of yin and yang is comparable to the plus and minus poles of electricity.

Chinese philosophy correlates all this world's opposites to one of these two poles, to yin or yang. Therefore day, warmth, light, man and so on, are assigned to the positive yang; night, cold, dark, woman and so on, to yin. This classification does not entail any kind of value judgment, however. An ideal state of health can only be maintained when these two poles are in perfect balance in our organism.

Yin and yang are the two energetic forces that, when combined, can be defined as vital energy or *chi*. This *chi*, composed of the two energy factors yin and yang, circulates in certain channels known as meridians. These energy channels run through the entire human body and are responsible for the functioning of cells, tissues and organs, supplying them with the life-energy they need.

Chinese medicine defines disease as a state in which there is a predominance of either yin or yang. Only the polar balance of bioenergy maintains the bodily functions in a state of harmony. Only the perpetual balancing of these two forces, of yin and yang, can create harmony and, therefore, health.

This means that disturbances which already exist yet cannot be detected by Western medical methods must be balanced by regulating manipulations. Chinese medicine makes use of acupuncture points, or energy floodgates situated on this grid of energy channels to restore the balance of yin and yang.

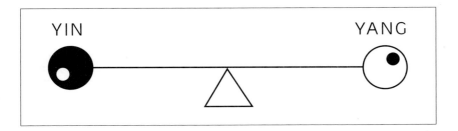

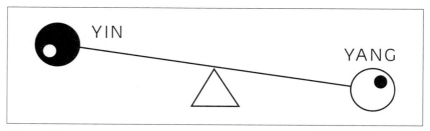

Yin and Yang Imbalance Expresses Sickness

Pure Vibration Energy as Therapy?

Natural medicine long ago discovered it is the most subtle stimuli — if used with accuracy — which produce the greatest effects. The "high potencies" of homeopathy, whose solvents no longer contain material elements of the active agents, have especially deep and long-lasting effects.

Through the information-content of the different frequencies, pure vibration energy seems to be the most appropriate means of influencing the energy-body. Therapy with colors and colored light is, therefore, of special significance in natural medicine, because colors represent nothing other than the different frequencies of visible light.

Colorpuncture, however, encompasses several significant new elements. The discoveries of biophoton research provide the basis for this kind of color therapy. Decisively new is the fact that Colorpuncture is based on acupuncture; therefore, it is actually an extended form of acupuncture, with colored light. This therapy is entirely based on regulating disharmonies at an energetic level. It is also the opinion of modern biophysics that the root cause for the development of any disease can be found here. Health is, quite simply, the ability of self-regulation.

In a state of health, the biophoton field, because of its high coherence (radiation bundling, as in lasers), is capable of responding with flexibility to all disturbances and influences, and balancing them out. It continuously oscillates between two states Fritz Popp, the father of the biophoton theory, compares to the Chinese yin and yang.

In a state of imbalance, in a case of health disorder, the biophoton field has lost its coherence and is "stuck" in the direction of either yin or yang. In order to stimulate the capacity for self-regulation (which represents the defense capabilities of the organism), the therapist must transmit some kind of regulating information into the body.

In Colorpuncture, this happens via the skin, which, according to latest research, operates just like our eyes: it is able to pick up light and color impulses and transmit their effects to the inside of the body.

The skin is not only a protection and a coating, it is also an antenna and a converting agent for any kind of vibration that surrounds us. In particular, this applies to certain skin zones and points which distinguish themselves from the rest of the skin by an increased "antenna capability". This is also true of acupuncture points, which, according to my research, have a special connection to colors.

In this context, the research, published in 1989, of the Institute for Clinical and Experimental Medicine in Nowosibirsk, then in the USSR, is of special importance. After several years of work, a research team under the leadership of Professor Kaznachejew was able to prove there are channels for light in the human body corresponding exactly to the meridians of traditional Chinese medicine. They discovered that the areas of the body which take in light correspond to the acupuncture points, and that the absorbed light is only forwarded to other points on the same meridian. This provides further confirmation of the effectiveness of Colorpuncture.

Man as Unity of Body, Soul and Spirit

The so-called metaphysical three-part body-soul-spirit division of man — which is actually a unity because all three levels exist simultaneously, function concurrently and depend intrinsically on each other — is not undisputed. Until a few years ago, medicine denied the existence of any connection between body and spirit. It was because of recognizing the influences of spirit and soul on bodily processes, and describing psychosomatic syndromes, that the medical community at least accepted a certain interplay between body and spirit. They still hesitate to acknowledge that the soul has any influence on the body. This is understandable because one cannot measure or weigh it, nor can its functions be documented by even the most refined electronic measuring devices.

In natural medicine it is assumed that the body is the plane of projection for any disturbances in man's "holistic system". This means that, in addition to bodily processes, any kind of disease should be considered as an alarm signal for disharmonies in spirit and soul.

In the same way modern physics ultimately defines matter as energy, it has been a basic principle of ancient Chinese and Hindu philosophies, for thousands of years, that all life is based on the harmonious vibration and circulation of energies. This life-energy (the *chi* of the Chinese and the *prana* of the Hindus) constitutes an energy-body that connects body, spirit and soul together. Any energetic imbalance will therefore affect all other areas of being.

The result of bioenergetic thinking is the holistic view of man and all his functions. Therefore, an isolated disease cannot exist: disease always takes possession of man in his totality, and that means that spirit, soul and body are all involved in the process. Each cell of our organism knows of the others and carries, in itself, the program of the whole. The information of life is all-encompassing.

The assumed bioenergetic potentials of the cells are certainly not visible, but, nonetheless, hold man's "matter" in the state of tension necessary to maintain the unity of the cells' material systems. Max Planck once said that matter, as such, does not exist. Matter is created and maintained by forces which cause the atomic particles to vibrate, while, at the same time, holding the atomic structure's infinitesimal satellite system together. The atom cannot be understood solely in terms of matter, but must also be regarded as an energy field; therefore, our attention must always be directed towards ways and means of regulating this energy.

COLOR INDICATIONS

Through the ages, certain qualities and symbols have been connected with colors. Similarly, general healing effects are attributed to individual colors, and derived from the "character" of that color.

RED
Red is the color of life, of the burning sun and of fire. Both love and anger, joy and rage are associated with this color. It is the color with the greatest power of penetration. It strongly stimulates the flow of blood and is therefore applied in cases of poor circulation and insufficient blood supply. Red is the color of the heart, the lungs and the muscles. It is the right color for treating non-suppurating wounds and inflammations, as well as skin diseases, chronic coughs, asthma, laryngeal complaints, anemia, weeping eczema and frostbite. It loosens the tongue, has a cheering and exciting effect, is stimulating and arouses passion. Red makes lazy people more active. Slow and listless children should do their homework under red light.

YELLOW
Yellow symbolizes the sun at its zenith, and is one of the hot col-

ors. It promotes digestion, strengthens the nerves, stimulates the stomach, and has a cheering effect. It strengthens the glandular system, makes chronic processes acute, and is indicated for diseases of the liver, bladder, kidneys and stomach. Yellow promotes learning and understanding in children and has a favorable influence on the intellect. All diseases of the digestive tract should be treated with the yellow. People who are discontent show a change of facial expression when exposed to yellow light.

BLUE
Blue is the color of peace and infinity. It is regarded as being a cold color, and has a relaxing effect. Blue is the color of the pituitary gland and the endocrine system. All diseases involving heat require blue. This color is also indicated for complaints involving suppuration, pain, plethora and congestion. Blue has an excellent effect on hemorrhoids. Warts disappear under the effect of radiation with blue light, and it is indicated for the treatment of stromata, certain heart diseases, sleeplessness and hemorrhaging. Blue affects the testes and is indicated for impotence, frigidity and menopause. Blue regulates contraction of the muscles, ligaments and tissues. Hyperactive children should do their homework under blue light. Blue brings silence, quietness and reserve.

GREEN
Green is the most common color in nature and is regarded as being a neutral factor. It is indicated for bronchial catarrh and whooping cough and, alternated with blue, for inflammations of the joints. All chronic diseases respond well to the intermittent use of green light, and precision work can be better accomplished under it. Green is indicated for tumors, ulcers and cysts, as well as for eye diseases and diabetes. It has a balancing effect and will promote feelings of contentment and tranquillity. Green is also sedative, soothing, and relaxing in effect.

ORANGE
Orange is a mixture of red and yellow and is the color of joy and happiness. It is indicated in cases of discontentment, pessimism, psychosis, depression and fear. Orange should be alternated with blue, however, when treating people suffering from fear. All sclerotic processes, such as arteriosclerosis and cerebral and coronary sclerosis, respond well to the color orange. It promotes the appetite and can be used in the treatment of emaciation and anemia. It is recommended for heart disease in general and cardiac insufficiency in particular. In

treating the effects of a heart attack or angina pectoris, however, orange should be alternated with blue.

VIOLET

Violet has always been associated with spirituality and, as such, acts on the unconscious, brings the individual spiritual strength, and promotes his awareness and consciousness. Violet increases the effects of all kinds of meditation and is also regarded as being the color of inspiration. It has a positive effect on the spleen and promotes the functioning of the lymphatic system.

This summary of the complaints that can be treated with individual colors has been compiled from the available literature on the subject, to which much has been contributed by color therapists and research workers from all over the world. I am aware of the fact that this list is probably incomplete. The above overview, however, is merely intended to provide the reader with an idea of the diverse possibilities for the therapeutic use of color.

COLOR-SOUND THERAPY

A New Method of Energetic Regulation

Early in my research, I was already considering the possibility of transposing the energetic effects I had observed with my Colorpuncture into the area of sounds. For, if every natural harmonious oscillation triggers a resonance in the human body, then this must also be true for harmonious acoustic oscillation. In the world of music we can easily relate to this.

Music is capable of producing moods in us. Depending on the type of music we listen to, we either develop feelings of elation or melancholy, are either stimulated or relaxed. Therefore, we not only feel an effect on the body, but also at the level of spirit and soul.

This realization alone was not sufficient for me to employ music as a therapeutic instrument. Music therapy, as it is understood today, is largely designed to involve the patient by active participation with music; for example, through instruments, singing and the like. My task was to find a way to influence the laws of energy flow by the laws of musical vibration. Clearly, it was necessary to create a state of relaxation in the listener in order to make him more capable of receiving the energetic information contained in the music. That was the starting point.

I knew it had to be possible to influence energetics via sounds in a similar way to colors; but I did not know how. I therefore had to find a correspondence between colors and sounds that, up to then, was not yet known. It cannot have been accidental that two people who were very interested in Colorpuncture came to me in 1986.

During the course of our first conversation, peculiar parallels emerged. Kay Korten and Ludovika Helm, composers and music educators, told me they had been researching the physiological effects of sounds and notes for many years. They had also been looking for a correlation between color and sound. It became apparent that Korten, Helm and I had been working towards a common goal from opposite starting points. It soon became clear that our different experiences and understandings could be brought together into a meaningful synthesis.

Converting color therapy into sound therapy allowed us to gain well-founded insights into the relationship between color and sound vibrations. On this basis we were able to create sequences of sounds in those frequency areas that correspond exactly to the respective color-therapy spectrum.

In this work two basic principles of energetics were taken into consideration:

1. the cell's resonance response to harmonious oscillation within the frequency areas known to the organism;

2. the energetic polarity, known as yin and yang in acupuncture, which expresses itself in Colorpuncture in complementary color pairs.

The decisive breakthrough of the new Color-Sound therapy was brought about by the complementary conversion of the color frequencies into sound frequencies, and by also considering the principle of polarity in music.

Our brain is the switching and organization center responsible for harmonious processes within the energy-body. It is accorded special significance in Color-Sound therapy.

Modern brain research assumes that our brain receives each bit of information in the same way a radio picks up wave impulses with complex frequency patterns. These patterns are recognized by the specific brain cells or brain waves so that different cells respond to different frequencies. The brain performs this selection process by evaluating the frequencies received and converting them into sinus waves. This is called Fourier Transformation.

In their frequency area, the corresponding cells then build up wave-fronts which overlap with those of others, thereby creating a holographic pattern extending over the entire brain. In the most infinitesimal space, one hologram can store billions of bits of information. The questions arise: What is it in the brain that interprets the incoming frequencies? Who or what is it that recognizes this?

There is every reason to believe that the information stored in the hologram is taken in, interpreted and passed on by the seven coordination organs of the brain. The frequency changes and transitions which are arranged in a specific way in each Color-Sound therapy, serve, on the one hand, to construct certain holographic patterns. On the other hand, the experience of recent years has allowed us to assign certain frequencies and modulations to certain coordination organs. This means that the frequency changes and transitions refer directly to the effect we wish to generate in the areas of the Thalamus, pituitary and so forth.

In this context, I would like to mention the "principle of guided attention". The wandering effect that can be obtained with ultra-modern recording techniques is important in reference to the synchronization of the hemispheres. Right and left brains are both activated to the same extent by this effect.

In the search for the causes of a disease, the same question arises again and again: Where does the disease-causing information come from? What is it that de-stabilizes the whole system?

At this point, I would like to repeat the most important statements bearing on this. It is logical that our material body needs life. However, to give life to matter pre-supposes information which, with respect to our bodies, regulates the innumerable functions of the cells. In all living matter, each cell requires information, receives information and delivers information. An unimaginable communication system, constructed according to a carefully thought out plan, accompanies man throughout his life.

Information, however, has to be transported; it needs a vehicle it can use, each second, to manage the interaction of all parts of our lives. The energy model of traditional Chinese medicine appears to be this vehicle. It can be compared to an irrigation system penetrating even the farthest corners of our being.

The essence of all life is information, but information cannot exist by itself. Only through the two factors, information and energy, does life become possible.

Owing to the research of Dr. F.A. Popp, we know that our cells emit an ultra-faint radiation. This radiation consists of light quantums and photons. The photons have no mass and move at the speed of light. They transmit their energy to free electrons and accelerate them. Nowadays, it is assumed that the interaction between photons and electrons is responsible for the exchanges of information in our organism. There is every reason to believe that the coordination organs of our brain are the superior authorities for this information exchange. As a consequence, dysfunctions of the coordination organs would have detrimental effects on the whole system. (See the graphic of the puppeteer on page 48.)

For me, the coordination organs are the information center which must be the main point of focus when searching for the root cause of an illness. In order to restore a blocked, malfunctioning system to its innate coherent response, regulating impulses must be applied from this center.

I compare such a system to the hierarchical pyramid of a business enterprise. I assign the head office, where all threads and information come together, and all essential decisions are made, to the coordination organs. As a consequence, the enterprise, "body", will be in danger if headquarters does not fulfill its responsibilities and functions.

The blockages we are talking about are therefore, in principle, information blockages; these information blockages automatically result in altering the holographic structure in our brain.

Dissolution of these blockages occurs according to the principle of resonance. This means that, from the outside, the inductive effects of the synchronous vibrations of Color-Sound therapy prompt the brain to its normal harmonious vibrational behavior, and bring the holographic structure back to the pattern appropriate to the whole system.

It has been discovered that different states of consciousness produce different brain frequencies. During waking consciousness, the frequencies of the brain waves emitted start from 14 Hertz. This area of frequency is called beta rhythm. In a state of relaxation or light sleep, the brain wave frequency slows down to 7-14 Hertz. This frequency range, called alpha rhythm, is induced by relaxation through self-hypnosis and other suggestive methods. In waking consciousness, the theta rhythm, which has a frequency of 4-7 Hertz, is only reached in certain situations, such as deep, healing meditation. The frequencies between 1-4 Hertz, the delta rhythm, is reached only in deep sleep. In that state, the waking consciousness is completely switched off.

With reference to the principle "As within, so without", it is possible to offer the brain certain frequencies it knows so that it shifts, according to the principle of resonance, into the desired vibrational state. Therefore, the vibrational changes induced from the outside will have an effect on the inside; namely, a change of consciousness.

The energetic music of Color-Sound therapy contains modulations of amplitudes and frequencies which, in the form of brain-stimulating sound structures, produce harmonious transitions from the beta into the alpha rhythms, and even into the theta rhythm. For this, the brain need not — even though language could increase the effect — perform any thought processes on its own; instead, it is carefully guided within its vibrational pattern. This imperceptible, liberating transition into complete relaxation feels extremely comfortable and cheering to the listener.

According to latest findings, specific functions and tasks can be assigned to the right and left hemispheres of the brain. Portrayed in simplified terms, the left half is the rational part; the right, the emotional. Therefore, the structure of our brains is also polar.

Both hemispheres are interrelated through an exchange of information. The Corpus callosum, which separates and, at the same time, connects these two halves, is mainly responsible for this trans-hemisphere link.

Imbalances in information exchange result in a cramping in the area of the Corpus callosum, which will, in turn, effect the coordination organs, Thalamus, Hypothalamus and pituitary. The information contained in the impulses transmitted by the coordination organs to the periphery

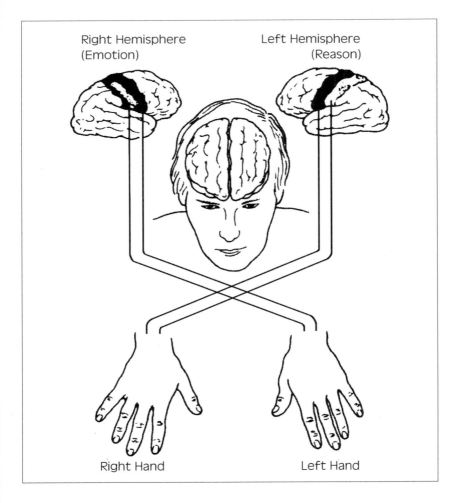

(body organs and systems) is altered; coordination errors result. These coordination errors manifest in symptoms that generally belong to the category of psychosomatic.

In this context, it is easy to understand how important it is to normalize and balance the information between the halves of the brain, as well as dissolving existing blockages in the area of the Corpus callosum.

The distinguishing factor of all Color-Sound therapies is that, through a complex recording technique, and via the ear, they access the brain in such a way that a synchronization of the hemispheres results. This regulation of brain functions is an extremely pleasant listening experience. The aim is to release such psychological pressures as fear and stress, and, therefore, to improve and eventually cure psychosomatic symptoms.

Let me explain the effects of Color-Sound therapy through the example of the Headache/Migraine cassette.

It is commonly known that migraines have a variety of causes. All forms of migraines — whether they are cerebral, the most severe; urogenital, liver or stomach migraines; or cephalalgias migraines resulting from pressure and tension — share one common characteristic: cramping in the brain. The pain is created when the cramp dissolves and an edema is formed. Therefore, on the one hand, therapy always wants to reduce the predisposition to cramp; on the other, to drain off the existing edema. In producing the Color-Sound cassettes, we looked at all migraine-forms and considered the factors (color qualities) that soothe the organs causing the pain, and therefore stopped the cramp-causing reflex from affecting the superior coordination organs.

Since migraine is accompanied by many psychological factors and, therefore, closely interconnected with the hormone system, it is evident that the coordination system must be in the foreground of therapeutic consideration.

All Color-Sound therapies start at the region of the Thalamus, because the Thalamus governs the channels of hearing and seeing. Awareness and sensation also come from the Thalamus. Therefore, it can communicate the impulses and information of the sounds to the other coordination organs. In the case of the cassette Headache/Migraine, for example, the coordination organs involved are the pituitary, the Hypothalamus and the Corpus callosum — the pituitary, because in any disease emotions play an important part; the Hypothalamus, because the inner milieu is also of importance; and the

Corpus callosum, because it is responsible for right-left migraines which result from an inadequate separation of emotion and reason.

Colorpuncture is the orientation for the therapeutic structure, arrangement and sequence of the sounds. The color-sounds are made in such a way that the same fields of reflection can be reached via the ear as would be possible, with color, via the skin. Therefore, for example, the Color-Sound therapy Psychosomatic Regulation corresponds to the so-called Coordination I of Colorpuncture. This therapy influences the entire coordination system and promotes hormonal regulation. Through this one becomes calm, because hormonal balance means emotional stability. Psychosomatic Regulation is, like Coordination I, a regulation of right and left, above and below, and is highly suited as an introduction into further therapy and as a daily prophylaxis.

I consider it important to avoid the "groove-thinking" common in today's medicine. Instead of talking about trains to learning, to joy and so on, which means overrating the tracks, one should pay more attention to the stations, to points of departure and to destinations.

My interest is not so much in stimulating or activating any kind of nerve route. The station does not care on which track the train arrives. It only exists, after all, because trains come and go.

Let us take the Thalamus as an example. Here, I can obtain the same results through color and the eye, or sound and the ear, as via the body; because surface sensitivity, consciousness, and channels of seeing and hearing are all governed by the Thalamus. I will never concentrate on the skin or on the eye, however, but always on the Thalamus. One only has to consider which connection or track leading to the individual areas of the Thalamus can become the starting point for therapy.

And this is the important thing about Color-Sound therapy: here, for the first time, the possibility has been created to decisively influence the coordination mechanism by means of acoustic vibrations.

In summary, we can say that Color-Sound therapy is structured, in principle, in the same way as Colorpuncture. Color-sounds are applied in the same sequence as colors. The quality of the sounds' energetic structure, frequency, modulation and so on, is such that the same areas of response are reached via the ear as, through color, via the acupuncture points indicated. The vibrational quality required to introduce information into the system determines whether Color-Sound or Colorpuncture is applied.

An advantage of Color-Sound lies in the fact that a deep state of relaxation occurs through listening. This de-cramps the coordination organism and therefore makes it more capable of absorbing specific information. Color-Sound therapies are extremely well-suited to prophylaxis and regular self-treatment.

ESOGETIC SOUND PATTERNS

"The world is sound!" This has been impressively stated by Ernst Behrendt in his book of the same title.

If one regards my Esogetic Model as a thought model for the living world, then it must be possible to convert this model into sound. That was my starting point in 1988. Development of the Esogetic Sound Patterns will be described in the following pages by Ludovika Helm who, in cooperation with Kay Korten and according to my theoretical outline, converted the Esogetic Model into sound:

"In the summer of 1988, Peter Mandel showed us his Esogetic Model. He outlined his conviction that the molecules of his model vibrated in certain frequencies and asked us whether it was possible to develop sound samples. In the years that preceded this experiment, Peter Mandel had already given us many unusual tasks; the successful joint production of the Color-Sound therapies was also the result of one of his singular requests.

"The more we delved into the problem, looking for extraordinary answers, the clearer became the path we had to travel. At first, we assigned one octave to each molecule, but soon found this was not the right method. We could not find a sufficient number of positioning points within the molecules. Various considerations led us to discover, in total, seventy-two notes which we could use for further experiments. We transposed these seventy-two notes onto two concentric circles, cutting through the six molecules at certain intervals. In agreement with Peter Mandel, we defined the Esogetic Model's symmetry point as the middle of the Formative Field.

"Even earlier, with Color-Sound therapy and with the Mental Sonar method, we had discovered, in our experiments, a symmetry note which can be precisely calculated in mathematics, as well as in the interval concept of Western music. We later realized that this symmetry note corresponds almost exactly to the frequency regarded as "the sound of life" in Indian music. Starting from the symmetry point in the Formative Field, we unwound the remaining frequencies to the left and to the right on both rings. From this, the following connections and realizations resulted:

1. the middle point of each molecule is always at a distance of one octave from the center-points of neighboring molecules;

2. the complementary note of each note can be found at a distance of 180 degrees from that note, meaning that the complementary tone note exactly opposite on the corresponding ring;

3. the circles of the molecules divide the note sequence from molecule to molecule on the first ring in a ratio of 7:5, and on the second ring, from 5:7;

4. on the points of intersection of each molecule with the two rings, and in its interior, there are seven exactly defined notes per molecule:

   a) a central note,
   b) a right connecting note,
   c) a periphery note of the second ring to the right,
   d) a periphery note of the first ring to the right,
   e) a periphery tone of the first ring to the left,
   f) a periphery note of the second ring to the left,
   g) a left connecting note;

5. a special characteristic was that, in the Body Systems' molecule, each note was represented twice and this, in a distance of six octaves.

"In relation to the extraordinary task set out by Peter Mandel, this theoretical-hypothetical base provided us with a solution: in the panorama of the model, the Formative Field and the body systems lie in the middle; on the left are the chakras and the coordination organs; and on the right, the Converters and the Transmitter Relays. In the panorama of the molecule, the central note lies in the middle; on the left and right are two periphery notes each and one connecting note. One can envision the panorama of the molecule as if one were standing on the center point of both rings looking outside towards the molecules. The ascending sequence of notes is always on the right side, and the descending sequence always on the left side of the central note. With this arrangement, something entirely new had been created.

"For example, the keyboard of a piano is horizontally linear with the pitches ascending from left to right; and if one regards Western musical notation as a graph, the notes are fixed vertically in an ascending order from bottom to top. We, instead, place seventy-two notes in a geometric system into different fields, with each note occupying its exact distinct place.

"We continued working with this arrangement and first made forty-seven test recordings: coordinating frequencies of intersection points; coordinating identical notes that lie within individual molecules, and so on. It became apparent we had reached, with this system, to what we call the "plane of symbols". In this way it is not only possible to interpret, in combinations of frequencies, geometric figures like squares, rectangles, triangle, rhomboids and so on, but also to interpret ancient archaic symbols like runes or mandalas.

"After the first positive tests it became clear to Peter Mandel and to us that we had discovered a nearly perfect system of converting Esogetic therapies into patterns of sound. According to the requirements of the individual therapy, we were able to combine the information of the individual molecules in any way we liked.

"The Esogetic Sound Patterns are, meanwhile, like the Color-Sound therapies, internationally known and extremely successful. The main emphasis of the concept of Esogetic Sound Patterns is in the areas of expanding awareness, new levels of experiencing, and increased abilities of perception. If one is familiar with the Esogetic Model, one can easily understand the objective of the respective Esogetic Sound Pattern from the molecules addressed and their expression in sounds."

These reflections by Ludovika Helm help clarify the basic concept of Esogetics. Now I will turn to the description of the seven Transmitter Relays.

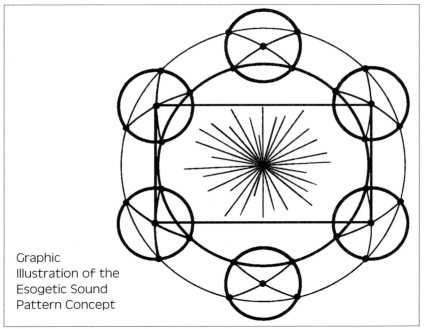

Graphic
Illustration of the
Esogetic Sound
Pattern Concept

THE SEVEN TRANSMITTER RELAYS

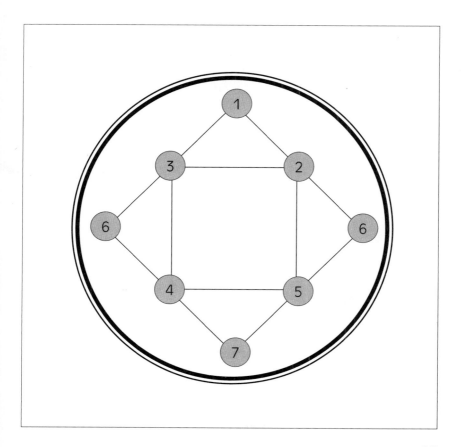

Through my achievements in EEA, Colorpuncture, Color-Sound and Esogetic Sound Patterns and, most recently, through the regulation of brain waves, I was able to observe, again and again, that therapeutic efforts resulted in immediate responses from the ill. In no time at all, the symptoms of my clients disappeared, symptoms which could not possibly be connected to all the centers manipulated.

I discovered that there are zones and points which, just by palpation and brief massage, bring experiences from the distant past to the surface; for example, childhood events. Furthermore, by testing those zones and points according to certain rules, I was able to ascertain the age of the person when serious traumas had been experienced. Through the application of Colorpuncture, especially through the color pair yellow (intellect) and violet (emotion-spirit) I could induce the patient to

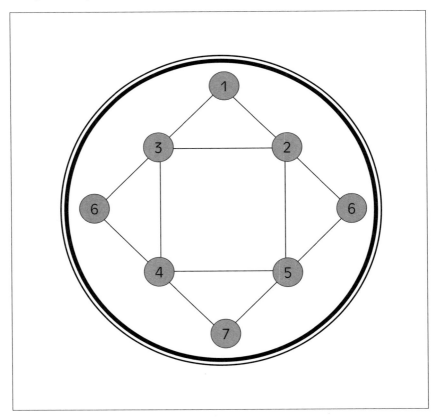

Transmitter Relays - Third Esogetic Molecule

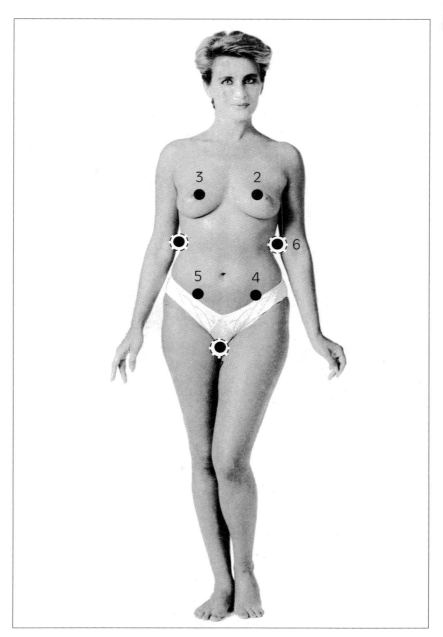

The Seven Transmitter Relays on the Body

re-process these experiences unconsciously. I later called this area the Relay of Experiences. The search then began for other overriding zones which might show the same or similar responses.

For the first time, I realized how infinitely sensitive was the arrangement of layers in the being, man. It often seemed to me as if I were renovating an old apartment where innumerable layers of wallpaper had been pasted on the walls. Layer by layer these had to be removed. I came to understand that under each layer an even older one could be expected.

It took an enormous amount of effort to classify my observations and the exclusively positive responses of my patients. It was amazing to see it made no difference the kind of complaint someone had. Experiments showed that a man, encountering this therapy, would suddenly obtain extraordinary access to deeper layers of his being. This would express itself through pronounced dreaming which, at the beginning of treatment, could be temporarily uncomfortable.

When I later learned about the brain model of Professor Rothschild, I understood what might be happening through this therapeutic process. Experiences that were hidden deep inside of us, and seemed long forgotten, were washed to the surface. The pressure which had resulted from these experiences and manifested as symptoms of disease, simply disappeared. For me, what was happening was like a miracle, and I often listened in astonishment when patients reported their experiences and the resulting changes in their lives. Encouraged by many of these situations in my practice, I started searching, and found the seven Transmitter Relays.

One of the most important motivations behind my research was my dislike of the popular treatment of chakras, extolled all over the world. I am not talking about the beneficial mental exercises taught in many yoga centers around the world, but of the physical manipulations which very often give rise to uncomfortable reactions in sick people. I have always been firmly convinced that everything we do or think in our lives has an immediate effect on the chakras; therefore, any manipulation, whatever it may be, will affect the chakras.

When one examines the Esogetic Model, the mysterious "wheels" become demystified. The logic of our lives demands such a system. If I place it at a higher stage in my Esogetic Model and attribute absolute information to this molecule, then there has to be a connecting link between the subtle and gross aspects of our lives. This connecting link, according to all my previous experience, is the Transmitter Relays of Esogetics.

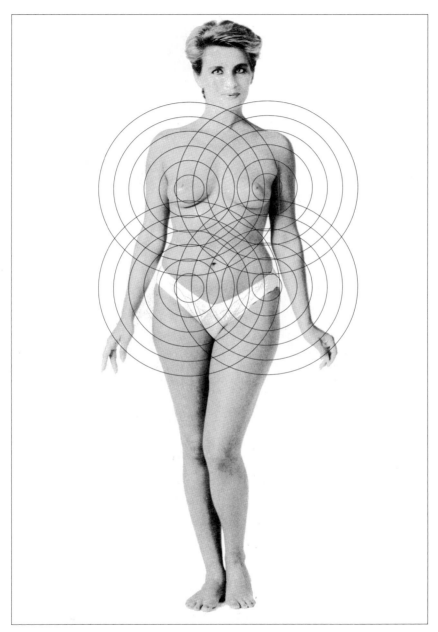

The Circles of the Transmitter Relays 2-3-4-5 in Front

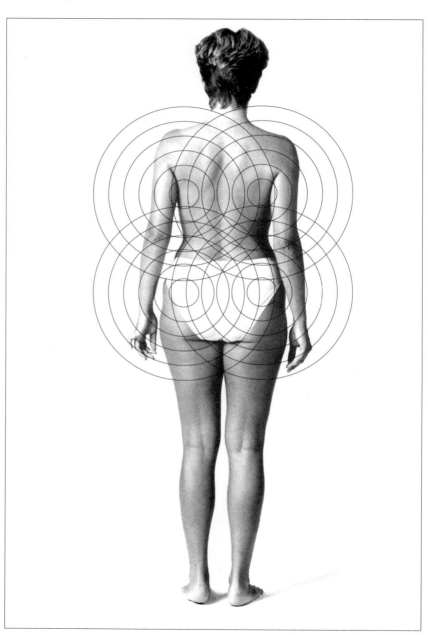

The Circles of the Transmitter Relays 2-3-4-5 in the Back

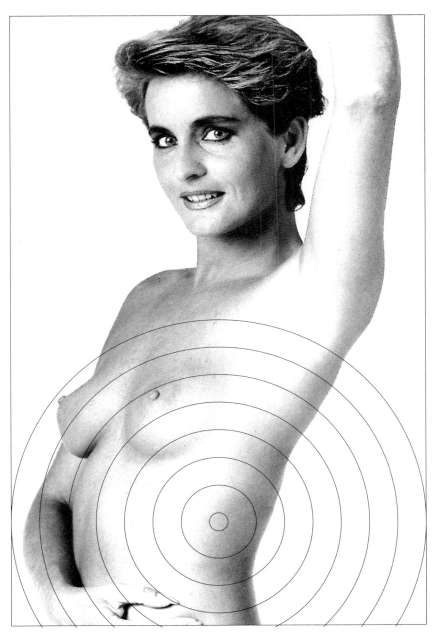

The Sixth Transmitter Relays with the Circles

An illustration of the Transmitter Relays will give the impression of a confusion of lines. As mentioned earlier, it is not easy to acquire complete knowledge of these relays. Once the basic principle is understood, however, the baffling interplay of lines and circles becomes less threatening.

According to experiential responses, I assigned names to the individual relays, designations to clarify their overriding functions. I call the first Transmitter Relay, which I will describe and discuss in more detail in the pages following, the Relay of Experience. I assign the second, third, fourth and fifth relays to cellular information.

Anything we experience and live through, reaches, according to a holographic pattern, into the smallest biological unit, the cell, and there manifests itself. This permits the conclusion that the individual aspects must be separated in order to gain insights into the whole.

The four bodily relays responsible for cellular information can be found in pairs on the body, like the sixth center. Here the connections to the yin/yang polarity become apparent. The relays appear on the surface of the skin like two wheels on one axle running through the body.

The sixth Transmitter Relay can be found at the sides of the body. I call it the Relay of Resistance. Here one can influence immune-biological processes, stimulate certain hormonal reactions and, above all, influence the garbage collector of the body, the lymph system.

The seventh relay is called the Relay of Instinct, and is placed between the legs. Here, special imaginative power is required to place the waves and lines of the circles.

Consequently, I distinguish between two Transmitter Relays which are disposed singly, and five which are double. An interesting observation is that the first and seventh relay have an immediate connection.

Let us now return to the analogy of the body as a marionette. When the marionette is not needed any more, it can be folded to save space. The following illustrations are designed to explain this principle:

The marionette is folded in the middle so the head touches the pelvis. This idea led to new and far-reaching therapeutic considerations. On the one hand, it became clear to me that the head, and therefore our thoughts, actions and rational processes, is connected to our drives. On the other hand, however, it became obvious that all experiences which manifest themselves in the first Transmitter Relay can also be found in the area of the pelvis and in the organs are situated there. I was therefore able to introduce new forms of therapy for migraines, for genital, bladder and intestinal diseases, for spinal disorders,

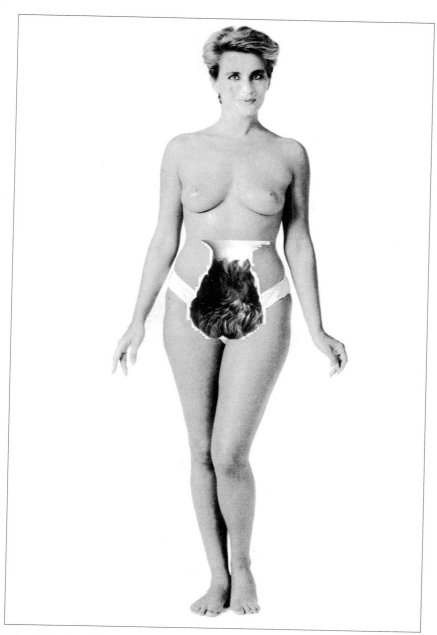

"Folded Man" (Front)

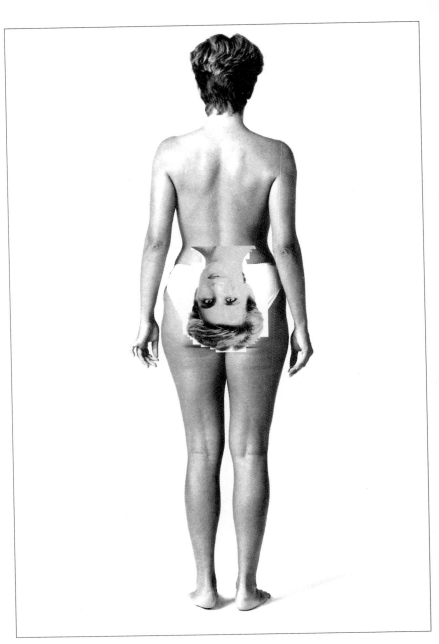

"Folded Man" (Rear)

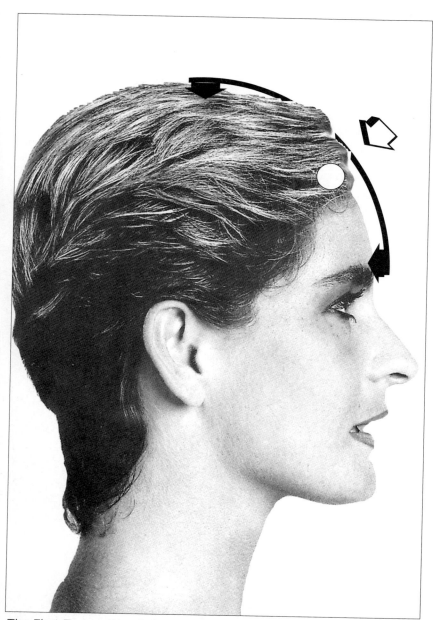

The First Transmitter Relay, between the Apex of the Head and the Mid-point between the Eyebrows

and so forth. These therapies are taught in my seminars and especially in my "Study-Group for Esogetic Medicine".

To clarify this once more: The curve of the skull is identical to the curve of the pelvic diaphragm. On the belly, below the navel, we find the cervical spine, and further down, the areas of Medulla oblongata and the back of the head. The pubic hair would then be the hair of the head. In the lower parts of the pelvis, the mouth, nose, eyes, ears and so forth can be found.

Initially, this concept seems unbelievable and incomprehensible. But if these considerations are converted into therapeutic concepts these statements quickly become acceptable. That means, for example, in treating eye diseases, one chooses the "eyes" area in the lower pelvis. This will yield much better results than usual forms of therapy. These considerations were very important for me, because I had to interpret the often mysterious reactions of my patients to find explanations for

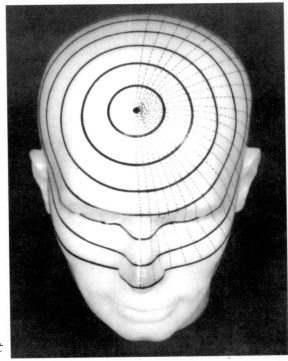

The Circles of the First Transmitter Relay, from the Front

these amazing results.

Up to this point my statements probably sound comprehensible; however, the following explanations concerning the first Transmitter Relay will seem almost incredible. I will confine myself to a description of the first circle. Perhaps the reader can form an idea of how much diverse knowledge and complex information exists within the entire system.

Just imagine we have seven Transmitter Relays. Each of these relays can be compared to a stone falling into water and generating ripples. To each relay I assign eight of these ripples or circles. That makes fifty-six circles in total, and if the double relays are taken into consideration, we must then add another forty circles. Illustrated in a drawing, it looks like a gigantic "salad" of ripples. On closer inspection, however, we can recognize that all the function areas of our lives are contained in it.

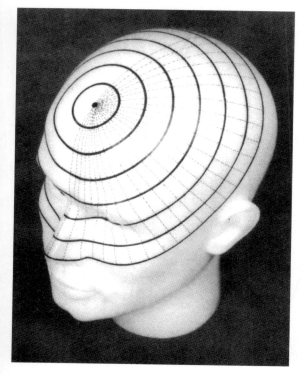

The Circles of the First Transmitter Relay , from the Side

The first Transmitter Relay can be found on the front of the skull. One should imagine a line from the exact mid-point between the eyebrows and the apex of the skull. Precisely in the middle of this line we find the center of the first relay. This is the point where the stone I mentioned drops into the water, creating eight ripples or circles moving outwards.

The first circle has a special significance. I assume that man passes through three stages of puberty in his development. Therefore, I distinguish between physical puberty (up to about age sixteen) and psychological and mental puberty. The entire process lasts, approximately, to age twenty-five.

All experiments show that traumatic experiences one goes through during the developmental phase from birth to age twenty-five correlate to diseases that appear later in life. Now, it is nothing new that in the soul-body polarity there are exchanges of experiential states, and that a man's suffering is connected to the harmony or disharmony of his spirit, soul and body. It is new, however, that the "points of disharmony" can be located and that, without the cooperation of the pa-

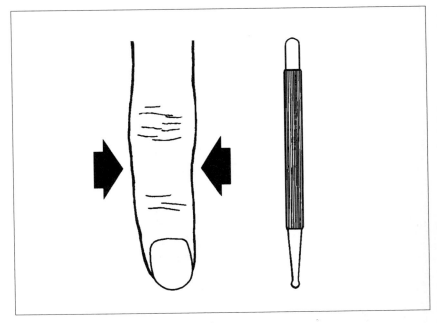

Index Finger as Measurement Unit

tient, these irregularities and blockages balanced out through Colorpuncture. As incredible as this may sound, whosoever undergoes this therapy will learn of its effectiveness.

Once one has located the middle point on the forehead, then the eight circles or ripple-lines follow. Each of these eight circles represents a self-contained response of the human being. I determined the width of the index finger between the second and third joints to be the unit of measurement for the radius of the individual circles. The first circle contains all one's traumatic experiences, both physical and psychological, between birth and age twenty-five.

The next drawing clearly shows the division of this circle. With a spherical tool the therapist palpates the semi-circle on the left side from top to bottom. The patient indicates those points which respond to pressure with pain. These points are then marked on the skin. They represent those years in which the person experienced strong psychological or physical stress.

In order to provide a more detailed description I would like to repeat: Starting from the zero point, the point of birth, there are

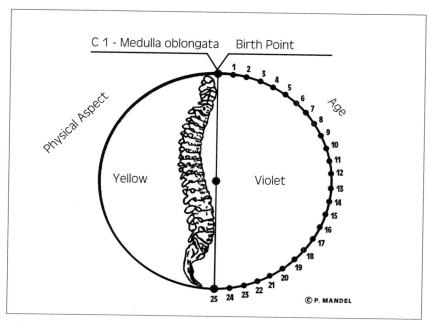

Division of the First Circle of the First Transmitter Relay

twenty-five testing points, each representing one year of life. The painful points that are found indicate those years in which a person went through traumatic experiences. These points are radiated with the color violet from top to bottom for approximately thirty seconds.

The right semi-circle refers to the spine, also regarded as the "axis of the soul".

Willy Penzel, who developed Acupoint Massage, has repeatedly said in his seminars, "If the spine is bent, the soul is bent as well." Medicine also teaches there is a connection from the spine, through the protruding spinal nerves, to the inner organs, and vice versa. Therefore, within this first circle, the spine is positioned from bottom to top. On the bottom is the area of the coccyx, and on the top is the first cervical vertebrae and the area of the Medulla oblongata.

The points that are tested in the second semi-circle indicate the physical-organic area where the blockages of the left semi-circle manifest themselves.

The understanding that man's energy flow moves in three different directions, and that each of these directions has a special signifi-

Directions of Energy Flow

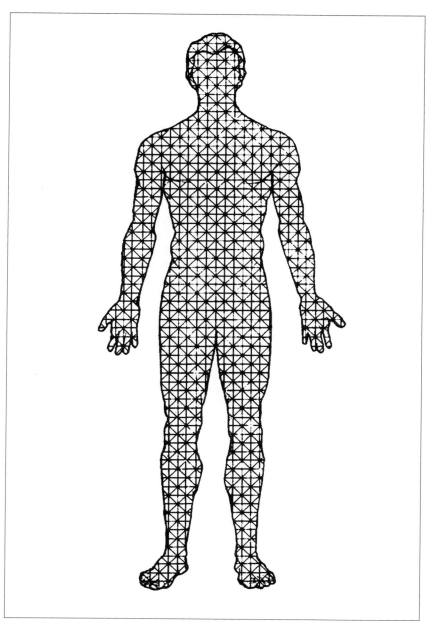

The Grid Network of Energy Flow Directions

cance in our lives, was a great help towards understanding the correlations in the first circle. The recognition and understanding of the directions of energy flow was a prerequisite for the methods I developed.

I assign the vertical direction of energy flow to the functional, endocrine areas; the horizontal direction of energy flow to all toxic-inflammable and reactive processes; and the diagonal flow of energy to all degenerative states. If these directions of energy flow are transferred to the body without taking the acupuncture meridians of the Chinese into consideration, they are condensed in an energetic grid which, for easier understanding, I have illustrated via a large mesh.

The density of this construction of pulsating energy may, ultimately, represent the legendary aura. In my understanding, it is the carrier of all information and all energies this dimension has to offer.

The fact that man is unable to understand or make conscious use of this information is no reason to dismiss it as mystical or irrational. In any case, it is a law that any reaction, no matter what it may be, must be preceded by information. We can inquire where this information

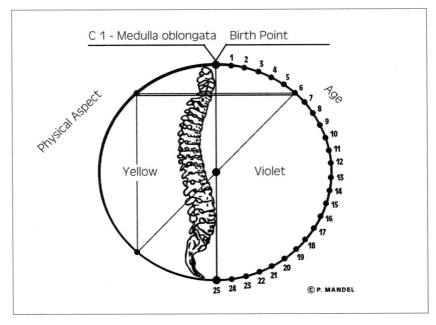

Age Six Illustration

114

comes from and why it exists; however, few answers will be forth-coming, at least on a so-called scientific basis. Ultimately, to me, it seems irrelevant to ponder which creator has arranged things in the way they are. I am of the opinion that the contributions many past cultures have left behind, and the ideas that arise out of these, offer answers to many of the questions of the civilizations that follow.

The informative-energetic law of the directions of energy flow is the starting point for all new considerations. It functions like a cosmic formula, therefore I also apply it to the circles of the individual Transmitter Relays. The following two examples, related to the first circle of the first Transmitter Relay, illustrate this.

First, let us assume a person experienced a serious psychological trauma at age six. If he is unable to compensate for this experience at an early stage of life, at some later point he will complain about diffi-culties in the lower back and belly. After some time, symptoms will also appear in the upper shoulder girdle; however, an examination of these complaints will not reveal any cause for them. The law of the directions of energy flow can help clarify this process.

If we draw a diagonal line from the age six point across the mid-point to the other side of the circle, this line will clearly transverse the area of the upper lumbar spine. Segments of the intestines are located in this area. If we now draw a horizontal line from the age six point to the other side, this line will cross the area of the lower cervical spine and the upper thoracic spine. This is an area that always contributes to corresponding complaints in the shoulder girdle.

The vertical direction of energy flow connects the two reflex points: the points of the lumbar spine/pelvis and thoracic spine/neck.

If we now draw a vertical line to the semi-circle of the years of one's life, we will hit the year eighteen-nineteen. If we test this point, we will find this is also a painful area. The year of age six seems, there-fore, to be mysteriously connected to a person's eighteenth-nineteenth year of life.

We have asked our patients repeatedly and their answers have con-firmed our assumption. It seems that childhood experiences are re-peated in a different form at a later point in time. Recent findings clear-ly prove that the path can be traced back even further. This means that we can even look, in this way, into prenatal time. This prenatal time manifests itself on the third circle of the first Transmitter Relay.

I was inspired by the publications of Robert St. John on prenatal massage, also called metamorphic therapy, to develop prenatal Colorpuncture on the foot. This method is the counterpart to the therapy of the first circle of the first Transmitter Relay in my daily practice. Here the circle seems to complete itself.

I admit these statements may sound incredible. If I were not able to convince myself of their rightness every day, I confess I would also not give them credence. However, there are many things in heaven and earth which man cannot, or cannot yet, grasp rationally.

A further example is intended to inspire the reader to self-reflection. Perhaps someone or other has a traumatic experience in his memory.

With reference to the drawings published on these pages and the procedure described, the individual year of age can be connected to the physical aspect via the principle of the directions of energy flow.

Secondly, let us assume a person went through a traumatic experience at about twenty-three years of age. People with such disorders will normally complain about pressure in the head and upper neck, and about strains of the coccyx, pelvic joints and all corresponding nerve connections. If we now take our directions of energy flow into consideration, we will be able to understand the correlations clearly. We

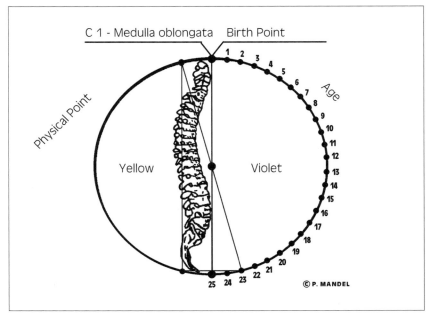

Age Twenty-three Illustration

116

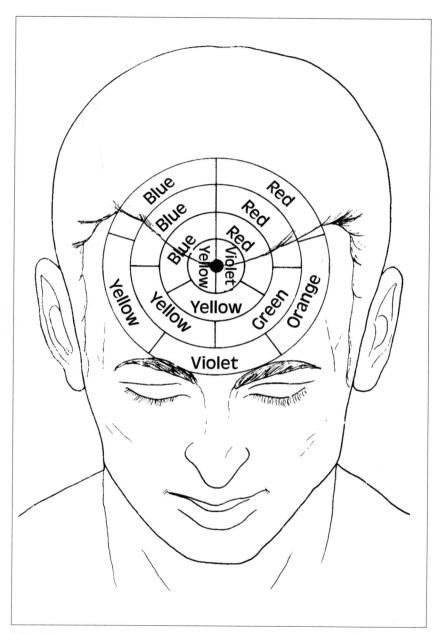

The First Four Circles of the Transmitter Relay and their Colors

will recognize, from a second vertical line, that this person must have gone through a trauma at age two.

These two examples are intended to clarify the principle.

In practice, the therapist's concern is not so much the individual years; rather, he starts his treatment with the first painful point. Naturally, further circles are also taken into consideration in the therapy. As when a stone falls into water and one ripple after the next is created, so it is with all circles of all seven Transmitter Relays.

A short description of the first four aspects of the first Transmitter Relay will clarify the power hidden behind the meaning of the individual circles. I have already described the first circle in detail.

In accordance with esoteric thinking, I place the three thirds of man's life into the second circle, assigning them the three primary colors, red, yellow and blue. I divide this circle into three parts. The first part is assigned the color red and symbolizes the aggressive third of a man's life. Here, he not only accumulates experiences, but also material things. In this period of time, he behaves aggressively and with ambition.

The second third corresponds to the color yellow. Yellow symbolizes the intellect and the sanguine, mobile temperament. Here, man brings order to what he has acquired and draws upon it.

The final third is stamped with the color blue. Blue represents the melancholy temperament, reserve and silence. During this time, a man looks at what he has accomplished and evaluates it, drawing the wisdom of old age out of this process.

The third circle of the first Transmitter Relay refers, as previously indicated, to the prenatal time from conception to birth and, in the first quarter, to even further back. Here, four colors appear, in the sequence red, green, yellow and blue. These colors also represent the four temperaments of man: choleric, phlegmatic, sanguine and melancholic. Interpretation of the phenomena found in the third circle is based on the meaning these four principles have in the repository of mankind's knowledge.

The fourth circle appears to play a special role in the system of the seven Transmitter Relays. With the first Transmitter Relay it represents the present level of wisdom. With the other relays, the fourth circle shows, for example, the law of the five Function Circles, the level of the twelve energies, the level of the twelve states of pain, and (I hardly dare write this) the level of the twelve astrological signs. It would fill several chapters of a book just to describe this fourth circle.

I would again like to emphasize that what I am setting down here is not fantasy. I am describing comprehensible, practical methods which are already part of the work of many therapists all over the world. I also teach simple manipulations in my seminars for laymen, where these Esogetic concepts meet with a great deal of enthusiasm. However, many of the Esogetic therapeutic methods should only be practiced by a therapist, because only a therapist can decide which of the various possibilities corresponds to the diagnosis he has made.

At this point, I would like to close the chapter on the Transmitter Relays with a summary.

Within the Esogetic Model, the seven Transmitter Relays represent the connection between the gross matter in our lives and the subtle. Each of seven central points is surrounded by eight ripples or circles. Each of these circles has a particular, clearly defined meaning. If all these meanings are taken into consideration, one gains a highly distinct insight into the human being. The therapeutic applications are extremely simple and are performed exclusively by Colorpuncture. It is of utmost importance for the student to apply a high degree of conceptual power, because this is necessary to understand the totality of the system.

Now I come to the molecules of the upper half of the Esogetic Model. The first molecule of subtle matter represents the chakras of Hindu mythology and philosophy.

THE CHAKRAS

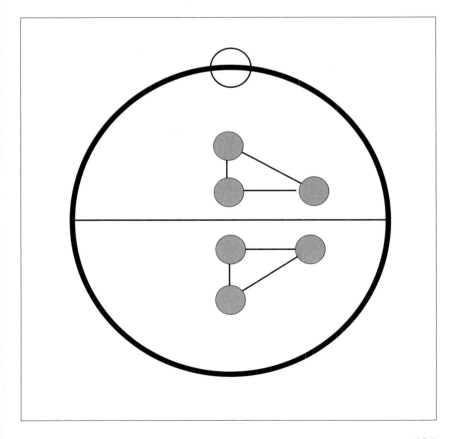

Mankind's greatest enemy is the ignorance and inexperience of so many contemporary people. They are unable to imagine that this dimension comprises many things of which they cannot yet conceive. If we cannot even imagine the trinity of our existence, spirit-soul-body, then how can we expect to be able to understand the really significant things of life?

Think about it again: Without information, this dimension and, therefore, man could not exist. So, first, one should investigate information.

Frederic Vester answers this question in the following way: "Information is an entity unto itself and is neither identical to energy nor to matter. It is therefore not subject to space or time. It can use matter and energy as a carrier, but always obeys its own laws. It can

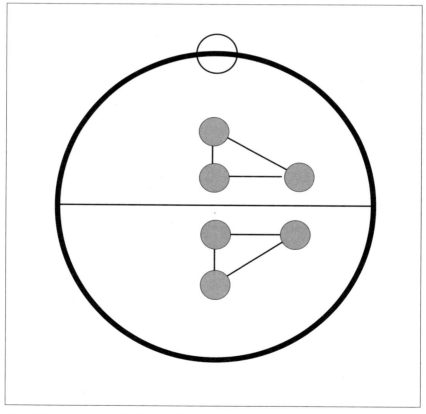

The Chakras - Fourth Esogetic Molecule

multiply itself and thereby set gigantic forces and energies in motion, without being energy itself." Therefore, information is part of all living systems.

Vester continues: "That which turns dead matter into living matter is the information that expresses itself in its structure, and not the matter itself."

In my Esogetic Model I assign the principle of information to the chakras because I consider the chakras to be the organizational model of life. Even if information exists independently of space and time, it still has to organize itself in one way or another.

In my opinion, information is not only part of everything that lives, but it is also individually designed for each living being. We can be certain that each human being is unique, and that no one in this world has a double. This idea points to the fact that each person possesses individual information designed only for him. We can draw the conclusion that the information shaping a man's life is an expression of hidden and overriding stipulations of the spirit-soul principle. We therefore assume that, behind this life, there is a program which unwinds itself from the moment of conception to physical death.

The information content can be compared to computer software. This software cannot function without hardware, and vice versa. Therefore, the result of this of software-hardware symbiosis is considered to be an open cybernetic system in which overriding stipulations lead to subordinate responses. In spite of all these qualifying factors, it is an incomplete system in which the individual being's program represents only the framework.

If we again imagine time as a stream, then all future evolves out of the past. If a person contravenes his own program repeatedly, this will then lead to a blockage of the overriding information, and trigger, in turn, disorders in a great number of subordinate functions. The person becomes sick; he destroys himself.

This can only be understood if the information responsible for the life-program is assigned, in thought, to a system. In Esogetics, this assignment is accomplished by attributing the overriding information that is independent on time and space, to the chakras.

I started thinking in the direction of informative energy centers when I investigated Indian philosophy, especially the chakras. All publications, whatever their source, attempt to explain the informative-energetic processes which reach into the higher dimensions of the spiritual mysteries. They recommended that people activate these centers their whole lives long — until the melting point of life, the death of matter.

It is certainly indisputable and understandable that the spirit is superior to everything else; therefore the Eastern suggestions of how to overcome disease are based on physical-spiritual exercises. When I attended the Ayurveda University in New Delhi in 1975, experiments with certain yoga exercises were being conducted to stimulate the body's hormonal responses. We were told it is possible, for example, to increase the quantity of cortisone in the blood through physical-spiritual exercises. I also received further information on the chakras; for example, one can aspire to putting subordinate material-physical aspects of our mind aside in favor of overriding spiritual information.

Meditation, yoga and many other methods can help man with this process. The biggest obstacle is that people have trouble switching off the mind and its thoughts in favor of deeper insights. This, admittedly, is very difficult, and only a steadfast man who performs the appropriate exercises with discipline will one day reap the rewards. Then he will have refined his senses and will be capable of perceiving much more than others. A new and fascinating world will open up for him. He will perceive and understand his surroundings from a different angle. But, unfortunately, as I mentioned earlier, this is not so easy: much discipline and exercise is required to reach this state.

Within the totality of Esogetics, I have discovered possibilities which help clear the path to the overriding information, to the chakras. The Esogetic Sound Patterns are such a tool. Here, man need only listen to and absorb the frequencies of the sounds presented. He will soon feel he is able to contact his higher self.

During experiments with these sound patterns, we had more than one hundred people listen to these frequencies simultaneously. It was astonishing to find that with more than ninety per cent of those present, these frequencies led to similar imageries. People reported they saw intensely colored clouds and sensed a certain detachment from their bodies. Others said that, in their inner vision, figures appeared with whom they had contact in childhood. This confirmed that the frequency choices from the Esogetic Model had been made correctly, because all of these tools serve to remove old blockages which hinder the information flow.

With this, man is able to access his higher self. After a certain time, on his own and without pressure, he will embark on his own individual path and will suddenly come into contact with certain exercises that will make him increasingly free and, therefore, happy. He will sud-

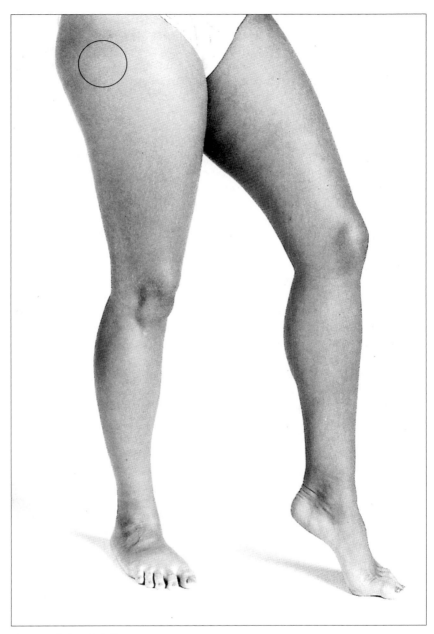

Zone of the Spirit

denly start perceiving more than his fellow man, because the information flow that has been freed allows him sudden contact with his chakras. All of this happens without stress or tiring effort. Then, without knowing why, he will suddenly come into contact with people and with literature that can help him further on his path towards himself.

Another helpful tool is the dream zones I have discovered, which are becoming more and more comprehensive. Let us once again recall the thesis of Professor Rothschild and his theory of the brain layers. He says that, among each other, the individual layers exchange messages in the form of dream pictures. The pressure coming from below must be released. Things which are blocked cannot flow. When the inner pressure is released — and this happens through our dreams — brain passages are freed for the flow of overriding information. If we continue dreaming, our own life-information will be revealed, by and by, to our waking consciousness. In other words, it will come into contact with its own program.

From the multitude of dream zones I found, five stand in the foreground. According to all my previous observations, these five zones seem to have a direct connection to the chakras and, therefore, to all life-information. They have to be treated according to fixed rules, which evolved over time, and the treatment is extremely simple. The following illustrations are intended to encourage the reader to perform these simple manipulations on himself. An etheric oil, the Esogetic Herb Oil, is used for activating these zones.

Let me first explain the individual zones. Their names were chosen according to the reports of people who carried out my suggestions over long periods of time.

The Zone of the Spirit is, in my opinion, a zone that represents the materialization of the being's individual program. By stimulating this zone, I short-circuit myself with my own program. The resulting dreams remove, on the one hand, existing "mental garbage" and, on the other, bring us into contact with the overriding spiritual information of our being.

The Zone of the Spirit lies on the outside of the left and right thighs where the hip bone can be felt. In the evening, before going to sleep, gently brush both sides and then rub in, for one or two minutes, three to four drops of Esogetic Herb Oil over a radius of approximately five centimeters. Afterwards, on the skin, there will be a slight cold sensation which will disappear after about ten minutes.

As with all the other zones, one should add the Mental Zone, as shown in the next illustration. The Mental Zone is also brushed briefly to stimulate the skin, and then three to four drops of the Esogetic Herb Oil are rubbed in. Afterwards one should go to bed.

On the second evening, one should work on the Zone of Intuition and the Mental Zone. On the third evening, one should treat the Zone of Imagination, and on the fourth day, the Zone of Intellect, always in combination with the Mental Zone on the back of the upper arm. Within a short period of time, one will start dreaming intensely — uncomfortably in the beginning; in the course of time, very comfortably.

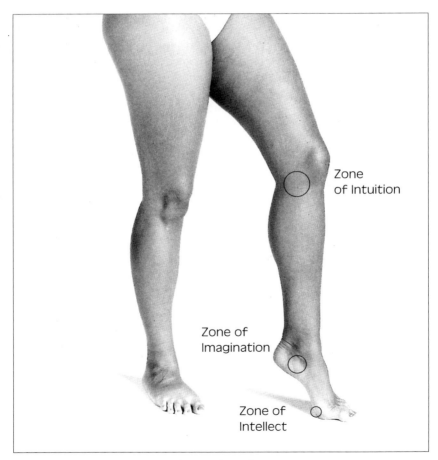

Zones of Intuition, Imagination and Intellect

The Zone of Intuition is located on the right and left inner sides of the knees. Its task is to enhance a person's intuition and inspiration so that he will become more capable of translating the needs of his own spiritual program. General intuition is also stimulated by this zone. Fairly soon, this will be felt clearly in one's daily life.

The Zone of Imagination is found on the right and left inner ankles. The radius of this zone is approximately three centimeters. Pure intuition is of no help to a person if he cannot translate it into pictures. Through stimulating this zone, one's power of imagination is strengthened. This treatment often yields remarkable results, especially with children older than six years of age.

The Zone of Intellect has, as its center point, the spleen/pancreas meridian of Chinese acupuncture. Where the Zone of Intellect is located, in the area of the bunion of the big toe, literature describes points which are important for psychological and physical constitution and development, particularly for children. Further indications for treating this zone are lack of concentration and coordination, learning difficulties, and a disturbed relationship to one's environment and to one's parents.

From the Esogetic viewpoint, the Zone of Intellect represents the final stage in this metamorphosis from the spiritual program, via intuition and imagination, to the intellectual understanding of what is released in this process. I would like to point out again that these zones should be treated by alternating them daily, and always in connection with the Mental Zone.

If a person wishes to enhance the effects of this treatment, he can listen to one of the Esogetic Sound Patterns after rubbing in the Esogetic Herb Oil. The assignments follow: Sound Pattern No. 1 to the Zone of the Spirit; Sound Pattern No. 2 to the Zone of Intuition; Sound Pattern No. 3 to the Zone of Imagination; and Sound Pattern No. 4 to the Zone of Intellect.

This procedure will soon help a person to contact his higher consciousness and to live a freer, healthier and happier life. The reason is that one comes into contact with the program governing this incarnation, and therefore gains access to the information I attribute exclusively to the chakras.

In this chapter, I consciously avoided entering into the complicated philosophy of the chakras. One reason is that the libraries are filled with this information. The other reason is that there are authors far more competent than I in presenting the comprehensive teachings of the chakras; for example, C.W. Leadbeater and his book *The Chakras*.

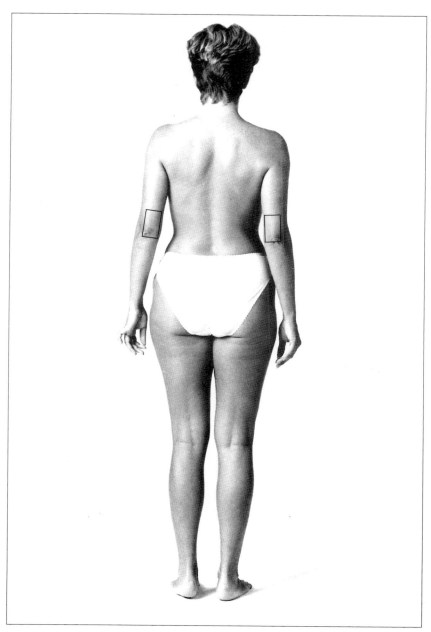

The Mental Zone

Whosoever is interested in the chakras can discover everything about them in this book. For my purposes, it is only important that the chakras are a system of purely spiritual information. Since information cannot exist on its own in this dimension, and because it is always symbiotically connected with energy, it was necessary for me to ponder how this might function in our being. I will now formulate these thoughts and transfer them to the fifth molecule of Esogetics.

THE CONVERTER MODEL

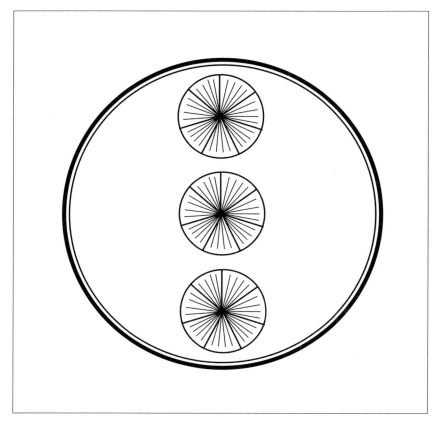

To repeat it again, and yet again: In this dimension information cannot exist without energy, and vice versa. If we wish to understand this principle, however, we will have to look at these two entities separately. In the last chapter I attributed the principle of information to the chakras, and in this chapter I will assign pure energy to its proper position in the Esogetic Model.

I ask you to imagine, in our bodies, three invisible suns, converters or stoves, busy twenty-four hours a day just producing energy. I place these converters in the area of the head, chest and belly.

I envision these three suns to be on the sagittal line of the body, connected with each other and, to allow all required information to be consistently effective, in contact with the entire cellular structure.

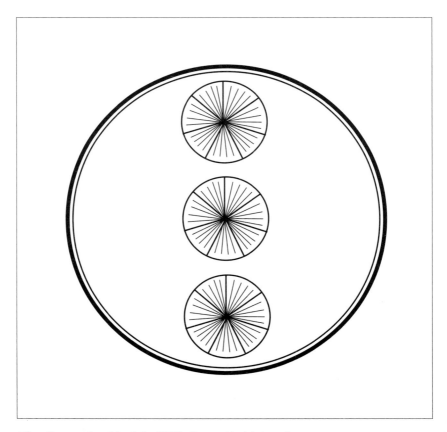

The Converter Model - Fifth Esogetic Molecule

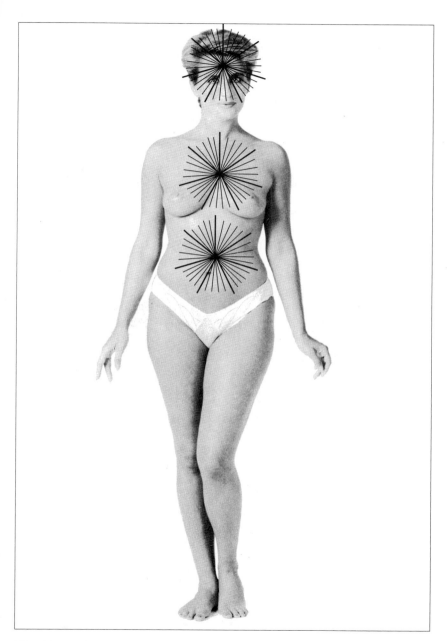

The Three Converters Projected on the Body

These "energy formations" have a special connection to our skin and to all information about the points, zones and reflex areas it contains — so to speak, to all somatotopia.

The three areas of the body connected to the concept of the three energy converters have specific tasks and relationships. I therefore attribute all reflex fields and somatotopia of the head to the head converter, the reflex fields on the back and legs to the chest converter, and the belly converter to the front of the body and to the points and zones on the arms.

If I am first able to envision that marks are left on the skin by information carried by energy from the inside towards the outside, then the next step, being able to read and understand this information, is not far away. It says in the Bible, "It is written on your body; it is written on your forehead." If I take this literally, I will actually be able, here, to encounter everything that has happened and is happening to me.

I divide each of the three body regions into seven skin areas, thereby creating a total of twenty-one areas. Within each of these twenty-one areas, seven points can be found. Altogether, this makes one hundred and forty-seven energy points, each of which has a specific field of response. I call them the Converter Points because, in my opinion, they deal exclusively with energy without influencing the information existing within that energy.

I mentioned previously the statement of Dr. Reinhard Voll that pain is the outcry of the tissue for flooding energy. I now take this literally, and envision these one hundred and forty-seven points I have found as simply light switches or dimmers with which I can either raise or lower the energy flow. In places where there is not enough energy in the tissues, I will turn the dimmer up; in places where there is too much energy, I will turn it down.

The system of the one hundred and forty-seven Converter Points occupies a central position in the training of therapists. In many practices, therapy utilizing the Converters has become standard treatment because it is simple and effective. On the one hand, I can operate these "switches" through Acu-Impulse; on the other, a short intense pressure of the thumb is often sufficient to induce a sudden release of pain in the sector related to that point.

I find it extremely interesting how the system of the Converters is able to reveal the meaning of sickness and pain. In those parts of our bodies where disease and pain become manifest, we can recognize connections into the depths of our beings. In the vernacular, over time, this has been expressed in such terms as "It chills me to the bone",

"It's a pain in the neck", "I can't stomach it" and "It weighs heavily on my chest". The questions arises: Who or what chills me to the bone? Who or what is a pain in the neck? Who or what can I not stomach? Who or what weighs heavily on my chest?

Pondering these examples, one understand the response the Chinese master made to a disciple's question about the nature of disease: "Disease is a thought."

It is we ourselves who inflict all disorders, pain and suffering on ourselves through wrong thoughts and actions. We should therefore regard our complaints as positive signals, because it is they who draw our attention to disorders in our conscious thinking.

The following example shows how such a disorder evolves from the higher to the lower, from the subtle (thought) to the gross (body).

All parents know that fear in children, although experienced unconsciously for the most part, leads to lymphatic reactions. Let us assume that the mother, father and six-year-old son are sitting at lunch. The mother asks the father, "If we go to the theater tonight, who will take care of our child? We don't have a baby sitter."

The father answers, "We don't need one. The boy can stay alone for once. When I was his age, I always had to stay alone."

The child hears all of this and, afraid of being alone for the first time, unconsciously tenses up. In the afternoon he will develop a sore throat and by the evening he will have a fever — therefore the parents do not go to the theater. Later in the evening the fever will go down and the sore throat will improve, and in the morning the boy will be up and about again.

I would like to give a second example that has to do with fear in man. In holistic medicine, fear belongs to the principle of the kidney/bladder Function Circle. The principle of the Function Circles appears in the thought model of traditional Chinese medicine as the five elements, and has also been described by Paracelsus as the five Entias or states. Along the same lines, C.G. Jung published the concept of these basic functions. No matter what the source, all concepts describe the same thing. It was Dr. Jochen Gleditsch who, out of all of this knowledge, developed the concept of the five Function Circles, the first of which is the kidney/bladder Function Circle.

On closer inspection of this Function Circle, one will soon understand the correlations I have described. The keys to this Function Circle are: ear, skeleton, bones. The aspects of this Function Circle are: stability, firmness, trust, continuity, affirmation of law and order, and obedience and acceptance of that which is. Going against these aspects will result in disorders of the organ sectors attributed to this Function Circle. Fear, fright, rigidity and, in particular, individual will-power belong to the category of this Function Circle. The lymph system will react to any disorder of the kidney/bladder Function Circle.

When I was young I was fascinated by the ways my teachers worked. When a patient complained about pain in the knee, difficulties in the area of the sacrum, coccyx or lumbar vertebrae, they would inject medicine into the tonsils or into the mucous membranes of the lymphatic tonsillar ring. Only later did I understood the connections.

The acupuncture kidney meridian runs along the outside of the body from the soles of the feet up to the first intercostal space next to the sternum. Its inner course governs the lymphatic tonsillar ring. This helped me to understand why a small injection into the tonsils of a patient could result in an immediate release of pain.

Within the system of the one hundred and forty-seven Converter points, there are groups I assign to the five Function Circles. For the following example, let us use fear once again.

Man often does not understand where fear comes from. Fear is related to the knee. In most cases I can immediately release knee pain, even if it is already arthritic, by applying short strong pressure on the Converter point of fear. The understanding that man, out of fear, does not dare take a step forward illustrates this clearly, because in order to take a step forward he has to use his knee. Being afraid means being constricted. A person who is constricted will never be able to experience the miraculous vastness of his life. By overcoming his fear, he will no longer have to endure the related pains and complaints.

The Converter points help us to understand the obstacles in the way of our being. Even if pain disappears through an Esogetic impulse, either an application of pressure or an electric impulse, it has nothing to do with healing.

Each of the Converter points relates to a disorder within the total being. If I remove the physical pain, this should still serve as an indicating signal that something is wrong with me, that my Transmitter Relay system is admonishing me to finally do it right — right in the sense of my own program, in the sense of my own higher destination.

I would have to fill hundreds of pages in order to present the one hundred and forty-seven Converter points and their meaning. In further books, I will certainly do this. This volume, however, is only intended to provide a comprehensive overview of Esogetics. It will have to suffice, therefore, if I only provide details on several points to convince the reader of the accuracy of my statements. I will now explain

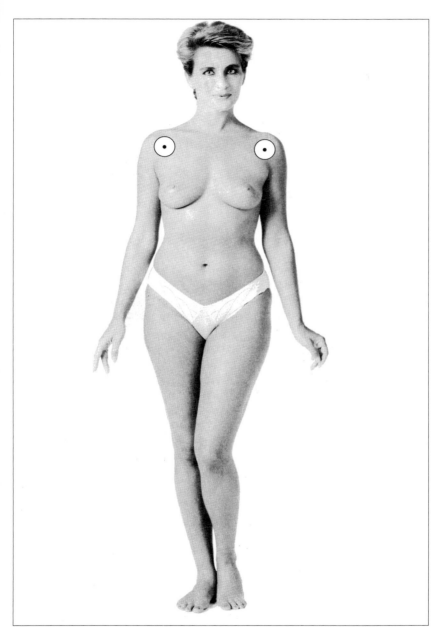

Converter Point of Fear

a few zones and points related to these remarks.

The Spine Projected on the Front of the Body
Explanation of Individual Numbers in Illustration:

1	=	Lumbar Spine, Sacrum
2	=	Iliosacral Joints
3	=	Hip Joint, Right and Left
4	=	Knee, Right and Left
5	=	Middle of Shoulder
6	=	Right Shoulder Girdle
7	=	Left Shoulder Girdle
8	=	Neck, Cervical Spine
9	=	Neck Right
10	=	Neck Left

In this picture one can see that the entire spine, including sacrum and coccyx, down to the cervical spine and back of the head, reaches the area of the lower belly. To the sides are the iliosacral joints, hip joints and the knees. Above the navel we find the shoulder girdle; below the navel, the cervical spine; further down, the head. I have described this picture previously.

Converter therapy is intended to remove existing pain through manipulation, but it is also to help to understand why one has this particular pain and what it wishes to say.

Where the sternum begins, the area of the sacrum lies. I call this area the Zone of Partnership. By this I do not only mean the relationship between the sexes, but also all levels of communication of which man is capable. Fear and worry, in whatever form they might appear in human relationships, always cause tension and pressure in the lower spinal segments, the sacrum, and in the area of the iliosacral joints.

Once again, I would like to quote the great teacher of energetics, Willy Penzel. He used to say that if the iliosacral joint is crooked, then the soul is also crooked. It is a law that joints cannot be worn out without pressure. This means that the wear and tear I see on an X-ray is not the cause, but the effect. Removing the cause is what is important.

All pain in the "axis of the soul", the spine, makes me ask myself again and again, "What 'chills me to the bone'?", "What 'weighs heavily on my chest'?", "What is a 'pain in the neck'?" In German we also ask *"Warum oder vor wem mache ich meinen Buckel krumm?"* or "Why or before whom do I hunch my back?" and *"Weshalb lass ich mich hängen?"* or "Why do I allow myself to slump?"

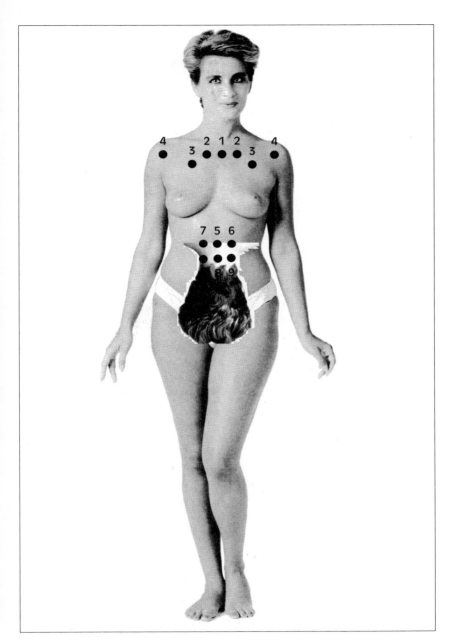

The Spine Projected on the Front of the Body

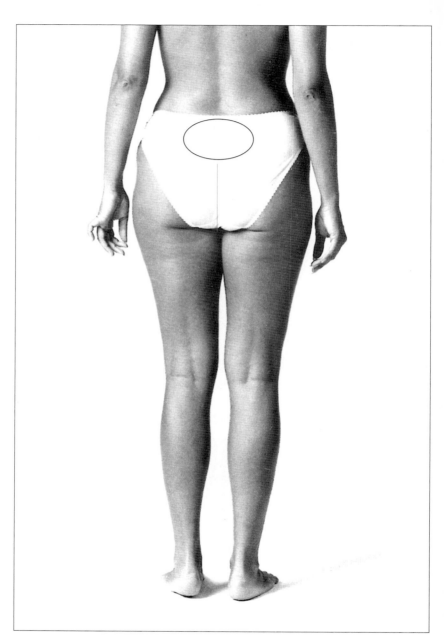

Zone of Partnership

These questions appear simple, but one has to rise above oneself to answer them. Only if I can find answers to these questions and consciously change — which means I stop exposing myself to stressful situations — will I be able to overcome the pain that might destroy me and attain to a happy life.

Life, in all its aspects, seems to be a game of questions and answers. Once we have learned this game, however, we will be at ease. Therefore, let's go for it! We have our whole lives to give to it. The Converter points can be signposts on the path each of us has to travel on his own. And knowing the goal makes it much easier to overcome the difficulties of the path.

Let us take a look at the early morning back pain so many people complain about. In my opinion, lower back pain in the morning has its cause in the intestines. The intestines, in turn, belong to the lung/large intestine Function Circle.

This Function Circle is the third within the five-fold hierarchy of Function Circles set out by Dr. Gleditsch. Here, the keys to this Function Circle are nose, skin and hair, as well as the sense of smell, a person's sensitivity, and his ability to "smell" danger. The aspects of this Function Circle include permeability, give-and-take, transformation and surmounting inner boundaries. The psychological faculties are intuition, inspiration and creativity; however, melancholy and the "woundedness of the soul", as Paracelsus calls it, also belong to this Function Circle. The fourth and fifth lumbar vertebrae, the area of the second, third and fourth thoracic vertebrae, and the fifth, sixth and seventh cervical vertebrae all belong to this Function Circle, as well as the bronchia, lungs and entire large intestine.

If we consider that, in the Chinese organ clock, the time of the large intestine is from five to seven o'clock in the morning, then the lower backache so many people wake up with is easy to explain. In natural medicine, serious illnesses like colitis ulcerosa — an often bleeding inflammation of the mucous membranes of the intestines — indicate that "woundedness of the soul" can result in intestine disorders and sickness. On the other hand, lower backache in the morning is due to obstructions in the drainage of the abdominal lymph.

For a long time I have been using three zones in treating patients in my practice. These zones are positioned around the navel and I call them the Aggressive Zones. The reader can try massaging these zones in the morning. The procedure is as follows: Locate the areas by drawing a diagonal line across the navel. On this diagonal, the aggressive zones are found at a distance of two finger-widths from the rim of the

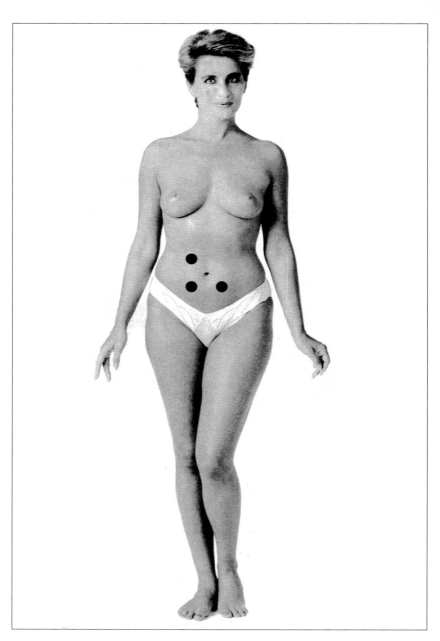

The Aggressive Zones

142

navel. With a relaxed belly, deeply massage this area in a clockwise direction. It only takes a minute, and then you will find your lower backache has disappeared or, at least, is substantially improved.

Yet, at the same time, you now know you have to take care of the "woundedness" of your soul. Ask yourself why, from time to time, you feel melancholic. Ask what limits you have violated within yourself. This is the actual meaning of treating the Converter points and zones: to look behind sickness and pain.

However, since one-way traffic does not exist, a man should also simultaneously treat the problems that surface. This means he should include treating the spine in his therapy. At this point, Colorpuncture can be very helpful. With the pyramid focus of the Perlux Colorpuncture instrument, one should slowly stroke the spine along the spinous processes with the color red, starting at the last lumbar vertebra and ending with the first cervical vertebra, and then down again. This is repeated five times.

Then, at a distance of one finger-width to the right and left of the spine, one should stroke five times with the color green, clockwise from bottom to top. Then repeat this procedure five times in an anti-clockwise direction. This is illustrated in the drawing below.

Next, in a horizontal direction, using the color green and starting at the fifth lumbar vertebra, one strokes the area of the sacrum and iliosacral joints down to the beginning of the anal crease. Finally, with the color red, one strokes lines one finger-width from the anal crease, first on the left side and then on the right, five times each.

Within a short time of applying this treatment, which takes less than five minutes, the reader will see how his life changes. Not only will he feel much less pain, but his psychological situation will also undergo a change he never believed possible. This is just an example of how my Esogetics is intended to help man remove existing blockages and disorders so he can travel his path freely and light-heartedly.

I would now like to describe three further possibilities derived from my energy model. They are a great help in becoming more sensitive towards higher realizations at the beginning of one's path. These possibilities should be included in self-treatment from time to time.

As everything else in Esogetics, these discoveries seem far-fetched, but yet are of outstanding effectiveness. I assign them to the Converter Model because, through manipulation, energy blockages are removed and space is therefore created for the overriding information without which life in this dimension cannot exist.

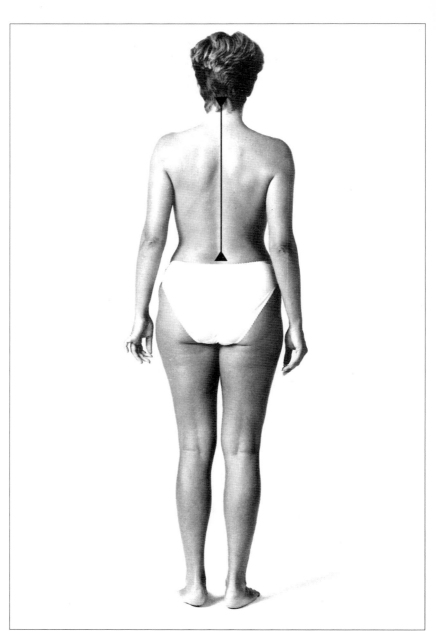

Spine treatment with Red

144

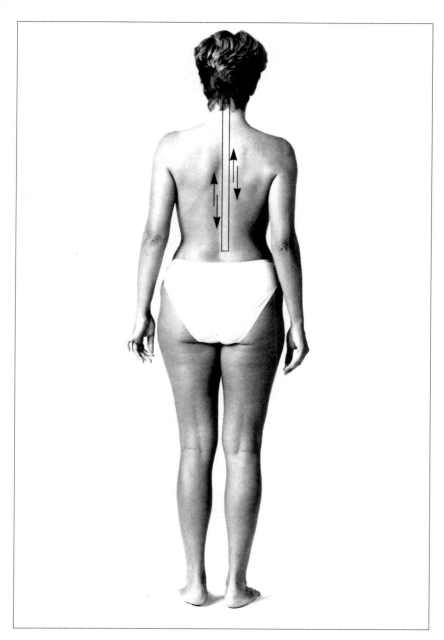

Spine treatment with Green

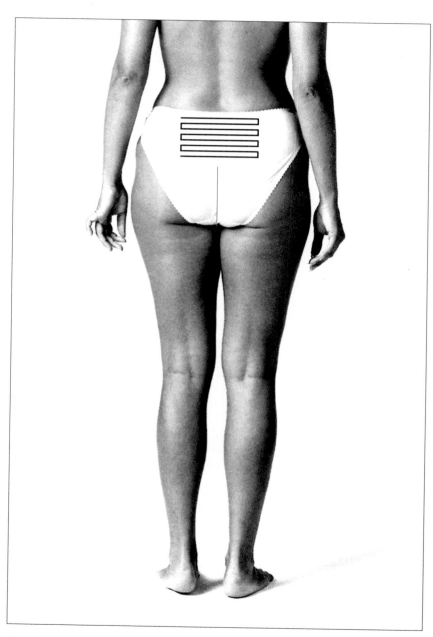

Horizontal Green Strokes on the Pelvis

146

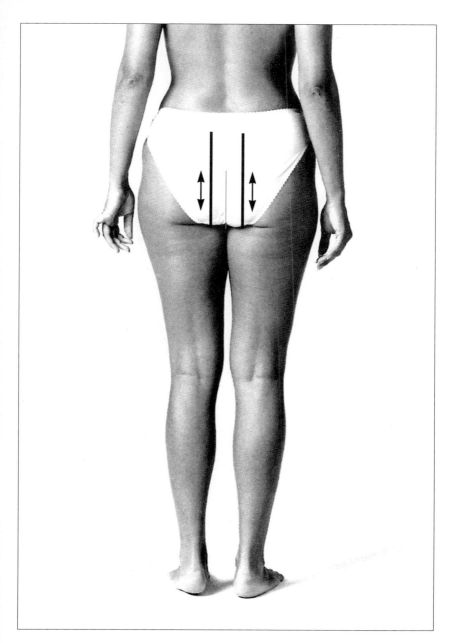

Treatment Alongside the Anal Crease with Color Red

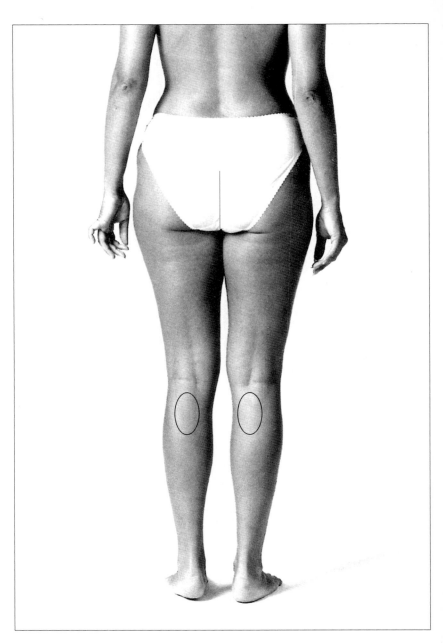

Kidney-Lymph-Fear Zone on the Calves

The issue of the first zone can be paraphrased by the common saying, "It weighs heavily on my chest." This zone is located on the upper third of the calf about one hand-width below the fold of the knee joint. It is about eight centimeters long and four centimeters wide. The zone is briefly massaged; then one rubs in three to four drops of Esogetic Herb Oil. This manipulation is especially effective in the morning. The treatment can remove pressure situations, either of a psychological or physical nature, felt in the area of the chest and lungs.

Here, we also find the correlation to the lymph. The lymph flows from the area of the head through the chest/lung area into the blood, which carries it into the kidneys for elimination. Strain of any kind will hinder this drainage; therefore, irregularities in physical processes will result and be felt in one way or another. So, one should not wait to treat this zone until strain is felt; instead, as a prophylaxis, one should rub this zone regularly to keep the flow moving. In this context, it is important to realize that everything that flows can be considered as healthy. Strain is only experienced if congestions and blockages hinder the flow, regardless of the cause of these blockages.

Six zones on the back of the leg represent a further excellent treatment in the Converter Model. These zones are especially suited for treatment by a partner. They should not be manipulated oneself, because complete relaxation is a prerequisite for the effectiveness of the treatment. I will now describe these points, which are situated symmetrically on both legs, from top to bottom.

The first zone can be found exactly in the middle of the line between the fold of the buttock and the crease at the back of the knee joint. The point in the middle of the knee crease is also regarded, in traditional Chinese medicine, as the point of gross physical toxins. The point in the middle of the thigh is attributed to subtle soul toxins. One hand-width below the knee crease is the point for regulating emotions. The transport of physical and psychological garbage can be stimulated from here. Another hand-width below, approximately in the middle of the calf, the point can be found which influences the body's biochemical reactions. Processes of combustion are stimulated here. The next zone can be found another hand-width below. Here lies the "Nourishing Principle. Here, the dispersion and examination of what is being dispersed, occurs.

The last and often most important point in this interconnected chain of points lies in the area where the Achilles tendon begins. It represents the polarity of giving away and holding back. I call it the "let-

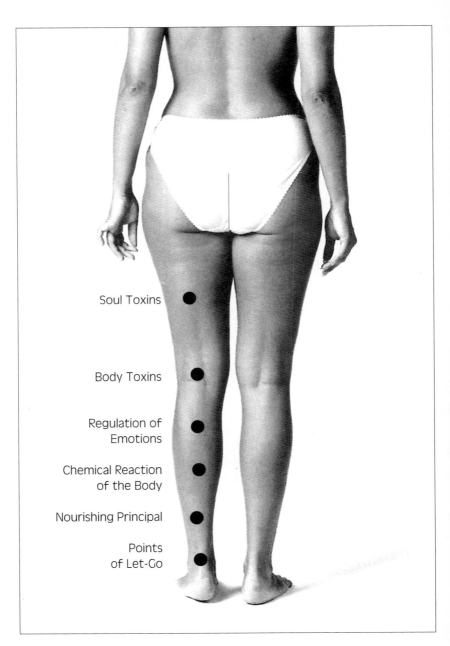

Soul Toxins

Body Toxins

Regulation of
Emotions

Chemical Reaction
of the Body

Nourishing Principal

Points
of Let-Go

The Six Therapy Points on the Back of the Leg

go" point, and by this I mean that this point especially effects people who, again and again, are caught in one circumstance; who cause the same situations, often through aggression; and who are unable to let go.

In my daily practice, this point is one of the most important therapeutic zones. I apply it whenever patients suffer from complaints of the rectum. In my concept of therapy, this point is also one of the most significant in the treatment of hemorrhoids, often experienced as very painful. Over many years I have observed that complaints of the rectum, including the sphincter, are connected to the inability to let go. The importance of this is illustrated by the incredibly widespread constipation of the intestines, which also belongs to the category of not being able to let go. It is often difficult for the people concerned to acknowledge this.

One should experiment by treating these points as indicated, from top to bottom, twice a week. One will soon discover that not only is the functioning of the intestines improved, but also one will suddenly adopt a new attitude to life without knowing why. In time, you will suddenly look at your surroundings from a different angle, and this may lead to a rearrangement and reorganization of your own life path.

The procedure for treating these six points is extremely simple and not restricted to any time of the day. Since the points are located on both sides, one should start on the left side with the point in the middle of the thigh. Afterwards, one should manipulate the point on the right side. This method of treatment should be continued with all the other points.

Once the points are located, they are massaged clockwise, by applying slight pressure, for about one minute. For this process, you can use the head of a pencil. Once all points are treated, the let-go point should be treated again at the end. Here, you should add a few short and intense pressure impulses. Afterwards, rub in one to two drops of Esogetic Herb Oil in all the points. With this, the treatment is complete. As mentioned earlier, within a short time, you will experience how effectively these impulses work on the whole.

The Converter Model of Esogetics contains a great number of further possible points and zones, all of which have a relationship to the deeper layers of human consciousness. It is impossible to describe them all here. Step by step, I will present all the information in further publications. At the end of this chapter on Converters, I would like to describe twelve points of special significance for daily life. I call them the twelve Awareness Expansion points.

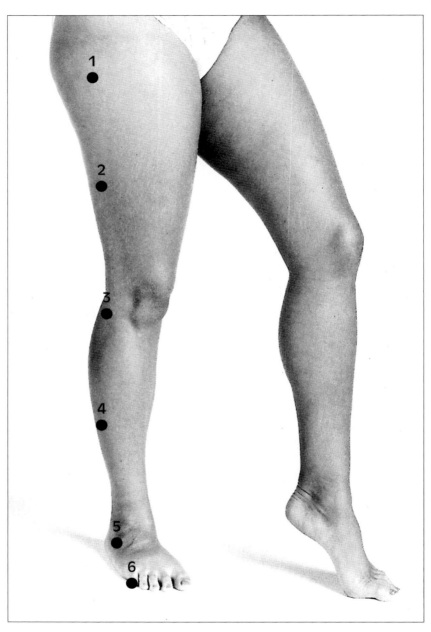

The Twelve Awareness Expansion Points

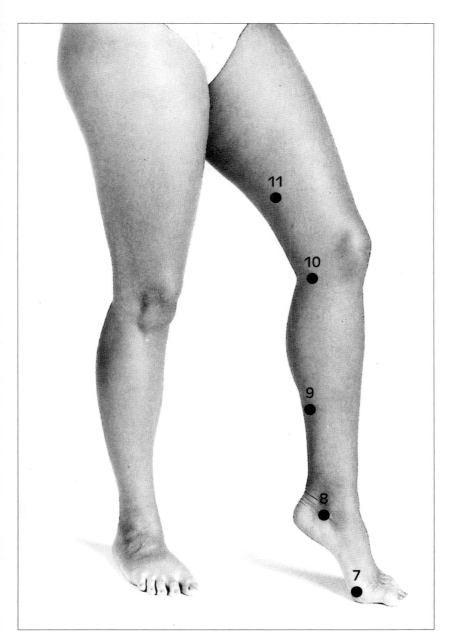

The Twelve Awareness Expansion Points

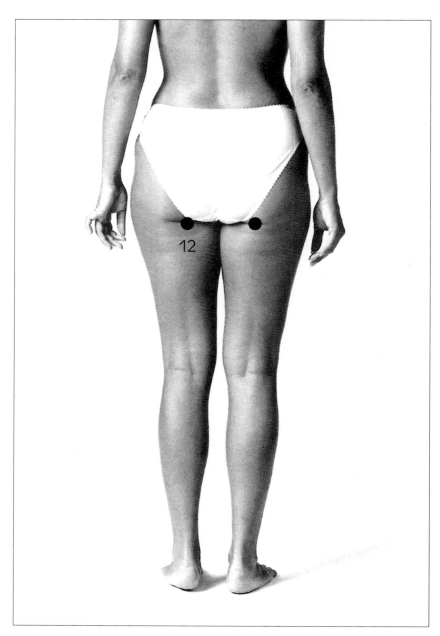

The Twelve Awareness Expansion Points

By now, the reader has certainly become accustomed to the seemingly outlandish statements in this book. The following points I shall describe are, in fact, incredible. I know from my own experience how effective the manipulation of these points can be. Many participants in my seminars have again and again confirmed the effectiveness of these points which relate, exclusively, to the deeper layers of our being. After several treatments, one will experience very intense and significant dreams, which can be regarded as indications to "that which is". After some time, one will develop "clear eyes", a clarity of vision towards oneself and one's deeper destination. This can mean a great step for the individual on the path towards his higher self.

I would like to emphasize again that the possibilities published here represent only a beginning. After some time, higher methods need to be employed in order to support the progress of the development that has been initiated. In the beginning, however, one should slowly start working from the bottom to the top in order to remove, one by one, the stumbling blocks our waking consciousness puts in our way.

Eleven of the twelve Awareness Expansion points are placed on the inner and outer sides of the legs, and the twelfth point lies exactly in the middle of the area where the thigh meets the fold of the buttocks. The first point lies at the top of the hip joint on the right and left sides. The second point can be found on the outside of the thighs in the middle of a line between the top of the hip joint and the crease of the knee joint. The third point is located on the outside of the leg in the middle of the crease of the knee joint. If one draws another line from the third point on the outside of the lower leg towards the tip of the ankle bone, then the fourth point lies in the middle of this line. The fifth point is placed on the tip of outer ankle bone. The sixth point can be found on the base joint of the little toe in the area where a small bunion can be found. It then continues on the inside of the leg, where the seventh point can be found in the interarticular space of the base joint of the first toe. The eighth point lies on the tip of the inner ankle bone. Now, again, one draws a line to the interarticular space of the inner knee joint. The ninth point lies in the middle of this line. The tenth point is located in the middle of the inner crease of the knee joint. Now, one should bend the knee slightly and draw a connecting line to the groin. The eleventh point is placed in the middle of this line. I have already described the location of the twelfth point.

This treatment should preferably be done before going to sleep. The procedure is as follows: Start at point number one on the left leg and massage this point for ten to twenty seconds. The other points are stimulated in the same way. They are treated in the sequence one to eleven, first on the left leg and then on the right leg. Finally, the two twelfth points are manipulated by massaging them intensely for thirty seconds, starting with the left point. At the end of the treatment, rub one to two drops of Esogetic Herb Oil into these points. If one possesses a Perlux Colorpuncture set, the points are radiated for ten seconds each with the following colors: point one, red; points two and eleven, blue; points three and ten, violet; points four and nine, orange; points five and eight, green; points six and seven, yellow; point twelve, turquoise. This enhances the effects enormously.

I am well aware this all sounds like hocus-pocus, and that some people will feel they should not take my statements seriously. I can only recommend, again and again, that you convince yourself by trying out my treatments, and then judge. I am certain if you follow my instructions exactly and with patience, you will become a real "Esogetician", which means, from then on, you will take yourself in hand and set out on the path that leads towards the higher dimension. Then you will no longer need anyone else to guide you. All you will need is trust in yourself. In the reflection of this trust you will then be guided further. New contacts with people will result, and you will feel happier and freer. Of course, one thing is indispensable: You have to take the first step!

With this, I finally close the chapter on the Converters and turn to the sixth molecule of the Esogetic Model. This molecule contains a great number of philosophical aspects of utmost importance for an understanding of the whole.

THE FORMATIVE FIELD

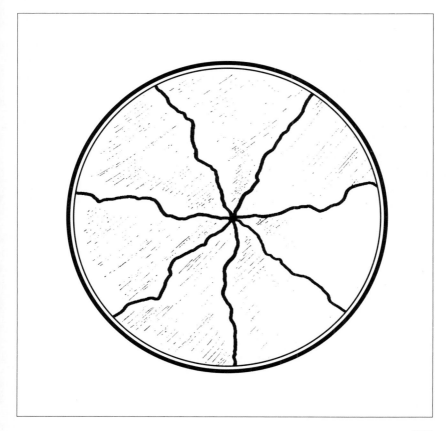

As mentioned earlier in the short description of the Esogetic Model, the highest molecule of the six-fold model represents the all-encompassing form-giving force. Here lies the complete plan of all life. From here, God's words "Let there be light" became reality. Here are all past and future forms of the three-dimensional world that is condemned to exist in polarity. Here all thoughts about the inconceivability of creation manifest themselves from the beginning to the end of time. The molecule of the form-giving force is synonymous with the universal Akashic Records, an enormous database in which everything that is and ever will be, is recorded.

In my view, this molecule contains the absolute information which transmits itself via the chakras, with the energy of the Converter necessary for the respective carrier. This process continues via the Transmitter Relays, and via the aspects of the Coordination Organs, to the material body. Through the connection to all universal information, the individual human being experiences the plan that exists exclusively for him, the plan he is constantly reminded to fulfill.

However, talking about a plan requires acknowledging an idea which, in the final analysis, is ultimately incomprehensible. And actualizing such an idea can only happen through the linking of endless partial plans. These partial plans find their expression in the infinite incarnations man has to travel to finally free himself from the polarity of this dimension, and to become one again with the divine from which, no one knows why, he once originated.

Memory impulses are constantly being emitted from the sector of the Formative Field to remind the being living in polarity to fulfill the partial plan. Despite all stipulations reflected in man's personal program, life can be compared to an open cybernetic system. Therefore, the path towards completing the present assignment is open. As long as the contents of the program are completed, it is irrelevant how one arrives at the goal of the class. If one looks at this "incomplete system", it can be compared to a frame that, in respect to quality and dimension, is forcing the painting to be finished.

The blockage of the overriding information arising out of the Formative Field results in an extremely large number of malfunctions in subordinate functional circles. This, in turn, causes disorders in all systems contributing to life. As a result, the development of consciousness is slowed down or blocked, and the primary information necessary for fulfillment of the plan cannot penetrate. The being's essential acknowledgment of its "now" can no longer take place. Feedback to the overriding areas will then no longer be possible either. This means that, even in innumerable incarnations, the frame cannot be filled — neither at the top by completing the imaginary picture, nor at the bottom by working on individual aspects of the imaginary picture. This is where Esogetic therapy starts working.

As above, so below! Again and again, one should recall the wisdom of Hermes Trismegistos. This is the starting point of my theory. Everything is mirrored in everything else. The principles of the Esogetic Model are reflected even in the smallest areas of our lives.

It is most important to understand that Esogetic therapy does not intend to work only with the ill. Sickness is certainly an obvious indication of a deviation from the plan of life, and therefore a clear request for change; however, Esogetic thought and actions support the gen-

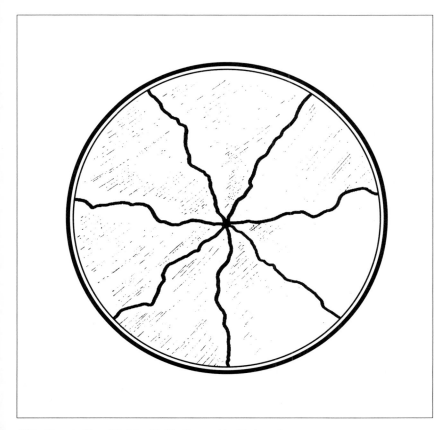

The Formative Field - Sixth Esogetic Molecule

eral understanding and realization of the relationships within the mo-del in order to free the light in matter, which corresponds to freeing the incomprehensible spirit.

Man's skin is the field of work. Here, everything that concerns the individual being is written. From here, one makes contact with the over-riding whole. For this, it is necessary, in order to make assignments, to learn to understand the individual layers. If things function from top to bottom, then it is a law of polarity that the lower must answer the im-pulses of the higher. If we thus decipher the writing on our skin; if we learn to understand that conscious life is composed of infinite layers, then we will come into contact with the Formative Field of the Esogetic Model. We will clear the channels inside ourselves for the flow of over-riding information.

Before this can happen, however, we will have to dismantle many refuse heaps which have accumulated over millennia. We will have to smooth the scars of the soul, inflicted upon it in so many incarnations, and remind ourselves of our past as light-beings. We may then be able to surmise why man, in the whole of nature's creation, has to stand between light and darkness; and why he has to experience both sides of the polarity, light and dark, good and evil. All opposites have their origin in the one. Just as there are two sides to coin, life's opposites are an immutable law as long as life remains in matter.

Professor G. Heuss says, "The spirit-being sinks down from above to below and endeavors to penetrate matter and to enlighten it." This becomes understandable if one considers the origin of matter as something totally without light, or absolutely black. The opposite pole is the complete fullness of light we conceive of as pure white. This is graspable and can be described as light matter in white and dark mat-ter in black. Now, if these two poles approach each other; if there is a lightening process on the path from matter to the spirit, then this will correspond to different stages of consciousness. Here the path leads from the unconscious/mineral to the dreaming/plant life to the awakening/animal to the becoming conscious/human to an ultimate spiritualization that is no longer bound to matter.

If light comes into contact with darkness, different shades of gray and fogs result, which I relate to the form-giving force. This force cor-responds to the primary gray out of which everything comes into being and which, in itself, must be overcome to reach to the dissolution of matter into pure spirit. This means the return to God. These concepts result from minimal hints one receives through contact with Esogetic treatment methods. This statement may seem presumptuous; however, my daily observations of sick people allow no other conclusion.

In my understanding, the realizations of my Esogetics are only a tiny beginning. I often have to contain a certain melancholy when I think of the discoveries and realizations later generations will most probably make. What comforts me is the hope that I may possibly contribute to these in a new incarnation.

Looking back at the sixth molecule, the Formative Field, we can summarize it as follows: Embedded in the Esogetic Model, we can find the key to all ideas which exist in this dimension and are waiting to become reality. These ideas are waiting to appear as thoughts in one being or another, in order to "take form" there. All of the primary information of this dimension is contained in the sixth molecule. Here, the first

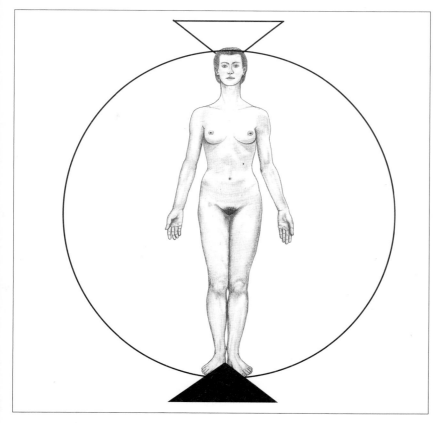

Human Being between Black and White

entry of the spiritual into the material areas of this dimension takes place. Ultimately, thoughts come into being here, and with them the polarity of sickness and health as reflected in the statement of the Chinese master.

I have no knowledge of a direct manipulative treatment for the Formative Field; however, there are indications that various possibilities of Esogetics can influence it. One of them is the color treatment of the soul line I have discovered.

This therapy, which is easy to perform, brings a deep peace to those layers of being that are often agitated. This tranquillity seems necessary in order for information to flow and become manifest. An unburdening of the troubled soul is achieved, and blockages removed which prevent the person from "rising higher". If I wish to develop towards the higher, I need the informative impulses of the Formative field.

The soul line starts at the edge of the middle toenail on the right and left feet, and continues along the leg and the area of the belly to the shoulder, then down again along the back and the leg, crossing the soles of the feet and ending at the border of the third toenails.

The procedure for this treatment is simple: One inserts the orange color into the Perlux instrument, then, slowly, strokes with the pyramid focus, beginning at the border of the third toenail on the left foot, along the course of the soul line as described above. Then the right side is treated. This rhythm is repeated three to five times. The treatment can be done any time of the day, even though it has been observed that its effects are strongest before going to sleep. This treatment is indicated in all situations involving pressure, restlessness, fear and desperation. If you try it out, you will come into contact with your Formative Field.

The most difficult undertaking in the description of the Esogetic Model is the description of the seventh aspect, the Transcendental Field.

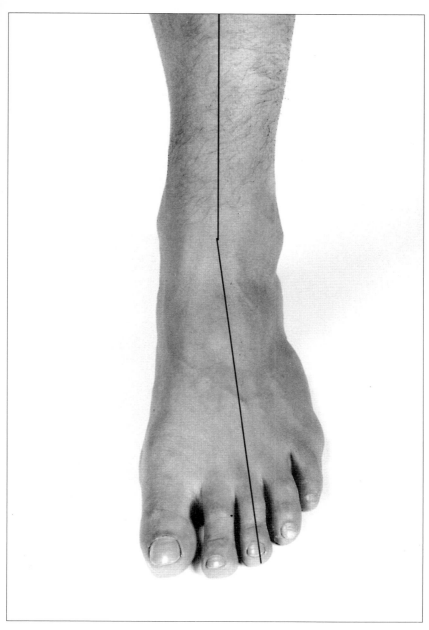

Soul Line on Front of the Leg

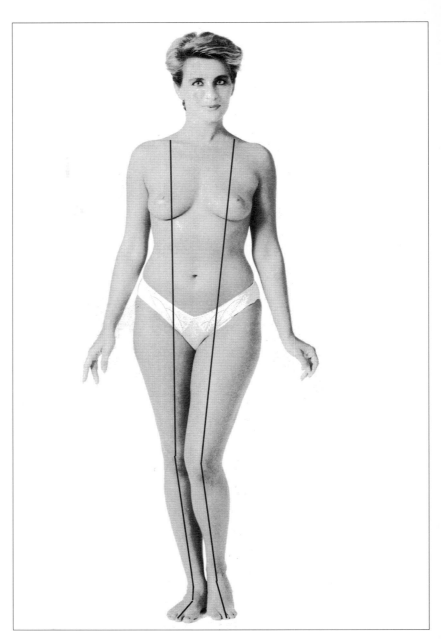

Soul Line in Front

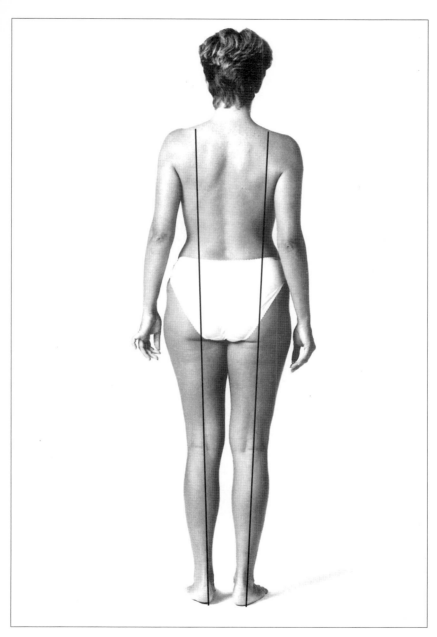

Soul Line in Back

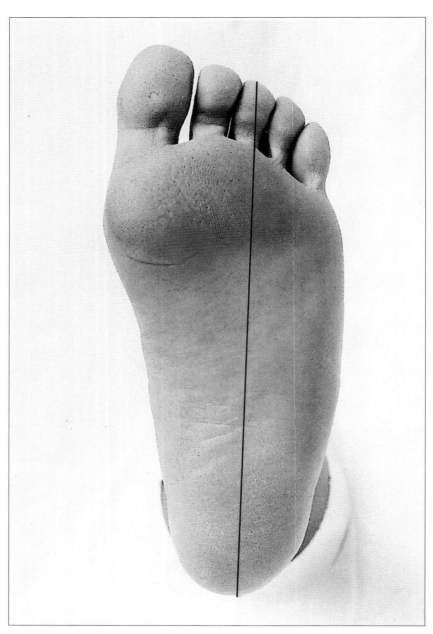

Soul Line on the Sole of the Foot

THE TRANSCENDENTAL FIELD

How can one describe something which exists beyond space and time? How can one understand that polarity arose out of an "all-one"? Is this concept beyond the reach of man's mind? I believe that the spark of the spirit in all that lives carries, within itself, the answer to the question of the transcendental.

Man, as a rational being in the evolution of species, places himself at the top, and since he has been able to think has always believed in higher powers. He has always believed there is an evolution upwards, ever higher and higher. It is impossible for his mind to project an end to this concept, because in his environment he has experienced that a new beginning always follows each apparent ending. Still, he cannot imagine infinity.

Down the ages, the afterlife was therefore identified with a god-figure to whom one goes or comes once he has left the world of matter. Man's longing for death, his desire to give up all polarities, all opposites — and no longer having to swing between the poles of good and bad, sickness and health, laughter and tears, and so forth — is deeply rooted.

Transcendental comes from the Latin *transcedere* and means "to go beyond". Transcendence is the expression for the "beyondness" of reality and being; it is, as such, the term for the divine.

In my Esogetic Model, it is the middle field which shines upon everything. From another view, it is the apex of a cone from where everything extends downwards through the individual layers and spaces of being. It is the pure light which, moving into darkness, creates the primary gray of the Formative Field out of pure black.

The pure information of that which lies behind the transcendental is firmly anchored in the chakras of the universe, of the world and, ultimately, of man. Here, contact takes place for the first time with the universal energies necessary for information to realize itself. Here, the divine-spiritual connects with the dimensional-material. Here, life as we know it comes into being. The process of splitting up into infinite forms requires a transformation in order to then descend downwards and manifest itself, through the Coordination Organs, on a physical level.

In reality, this process of spirit descending into matter is more complicated, and incomprehensible to the human mind. Still, the human being who sets out on the arduous path towards the inner will be capable of understanding, step by step, the network of divine-spiritual information. This has always been so. Man has always felt there is something beyond him towards which he must evolve and to which he can ascend, finally leaving behind all the suffering and tears of his material existence.

The curse of physical existence and the longing for liberation from the yoke of matter has, at all times, brought the term "God" into this dimension. Out of this, all religions have come into being. The origin of many of these religions fades away into the dim and misty past. This is the case, for example, with Hinduism. With all other great world religions, the founder is known: Buddhism, Islam, Christianity. In these religions the term "God" is personalized; God is transferred into the material world and therefore into one's own polarity. In some religions, the concept of a resting and inactive God is preferred; in others, there exists the concept of an active and creative God. In order to synthesize

Transcendental Field - Seventh Esogetic Molecule

these concepts, mediating entities and spiritual hierarchies, regarded as aspects of God, were required.

In my conception, transcendence represents a barrier behind which the incomprehensible divine lies. This barrier has to be overcome. It is the true task of man to ascend into the light of his own existence. It is his task to develop his light (spirit) and liberate it from matter in order to go beyond the last barrier to the experience of the transcendental, the divine, and merge with it.

This path is particularly difficult for the human being imprisoned in polarity, because to rise higher and reach his center, he has to push aside more and more the mind he so favors. Again, this sounds like surrendering the self, the personality that has been so arduously constructed and which man uses in his environment.

Man must turn himself from the outer towards the inner to be able to ascend to the transcendental. If he does this, he will become a mystic.

The word "mystic" comes from the Greek word *myein*, which means "closing the eyes". If one wishes to go inside, one must close the eyes and go into stillness, switching off the concerns of everyday life and the outer world, descending deeper and deeper inside oneself in order to find one's own light, one's own spirit. This process is called meditation. Meditation is the path from the outer towards the inner. This path leads to an expansion of consciousness, to a transformation of the being, to a gradual enlightenment and, ultimately, to a going beyond matter. The surmounting of all material structures is the prerequisite for going beyond the barrier to the transcendental and experiencing union with the divine.

In Hinduism, the individual soul (Atman) unites with the soul of the world (Brahman). Buddhism strives for the entry into *nirvana*; in Taoism it is union with the unfathomable Tao. In all religions, union with the divine is the path towards God, and proximity to God is the uppermost goal of all creatures and men. The variety of the different paths is ultimately insignificant, because once one has gone beyond the barrier, the question of "how" is without value.

So, if everything must develop from the lower towards the higher; if everything must rise to the last frontier, we have to consider what we must transcend to reach to God. What is the transcendental, and what is the absolute beyond? Is it God himself? Is it divine space, the Garden of Eden? Nobody knows, and yet we will experience it one day.

It is conceivable that this dimension, this world of matter, is a shadow of what we call the absolute beyond. If this is so, then the divine can be found here and now in all that lives and exists; therefore, in us as well.

We have to turn away from our suffering and sickness because they are the hindrances on our path towards the inner. We have to bid farewell to those frustrations and fears which prevent us from progressing and from coming into contact with our higher selves. All negative is the result of the positive, and vice versa. Through understanding and accepting both, we start on our path towards the inner: we close our eyes; we become mystics. With this, we set out on the path which, however long it may be, inevitably leads to the transcendental, to God.

Therefore the Esogetic Model is, from bottom to top, a guideline or hand-rail on this path. The fact that the lower is the same as the higher helps us realize that the body has to be cleansed first; then, no matter how many incarnations it may take, the path can rise beyond the material body and reach the transcendental.

My Esogetics can certainly represent a beginning for all. It is a teaching that can show man, in an almost playful way, who and what he really is. Esogetics may be able to bring some people into contact with themselves for the first time without a constant rational analysis of the process. Through simple manipulations, a man who wants to liberate himself from his darkness can contact his light. He will learn to understand that sickness is his own product: he keeps running against the same walls and hurting himself until he discovers that there is a door through which he can easily reach into the other room. Once he has understood the principle of the door, he will probably never run against the wall again. But exactly this seems to be difficult for man.

Esogetic therapies, from simple pressure manipulations to colors and sounds, are connected to a map written on the skin, one which can be deciphered through reflex fields that are complete in themselves. I am convinced that one day this map will not only be understood, with respect to the body, but also that this map will also be understood to carry all aspects of the spirit and of light, including the transcendence of matter, the barrier to the transcendental. The possibility of transcendence is inscribed in everything that exists. We have to set out on the path to find the "book of God" within ourselves.

Many people who sing the high song of esoterics in circles and societies are so far away from really walking on that path. The elementary fact that the path to the top begins at the bottom directs our focus to the body, to our polarity. We must learn to understand this polarity, the law of this dimension, to become healthy in both body and soul. Then we will discover the spark of the spirit within ourselves that enables us to cross the frontier to the transcendental.

The description of the seventh molecule of Esogetics should not stop here. So much remains unsaid; so much wants to surface and be understood. However, I believe that this short contact with the term "transcendental" will suffice to prompt the reader to listen inside himself so, there, he may find some small hints towards the abstract. Only if one has come into contact with these few small impulses can one comprehend the benediction that ensues from them.

And so, the seven-fold model of Esogetics is described in its various meanings. With this book I have intended to describe the interplay of the forces which reach from the lower physical aspects up to reflections on the principle of God. The therapeutic suggestions are intended to help one experience these forces oneself — especially those of the molecules of the Coordination Organs and of the Converters.

At the end of this book, I would like to present a few more examples with instructions, so the reader can further convince him-self of the effectiveness of the seven-fold model. I would again like to clarify and emphasize that I do not consider myself in possession of the absolute truth. I know there are many others who try to bring man closer to a state of well-being. The Esogetic path is only one among many; however, it is a path which enhances the understanding of one's own individuality, which reveals secrets through the body. This path is ultimately capable of clearing the way towards the reality of one's own being by eliminating suffering and pain.

In this world, man can only be healed by himself. If he understands that nobody on the outside is to blame; if he understands that he himself is the source of all his emotions, then he is already on the path towards his higher self. And then, furthermore, if he goes into silence, closing his eyes and letting his mind and its endless thoughts pass by without paying attention to them, he will go deeper and deeper inside until he can see the light within his matter, which he can then release. The prerequisite for this, however, is that he understand and learn to deal with his physical reality. He will realize the outer environment is nothing but a mirror of himself.

Esogetic thought looks at all physical aspects separately and, in order to realize the individuality of the being, relates the different functions to the corresponding psychological responses. In further publications in the Esogetics series, I will concern myself with illuminating, step by step, the complete system of physical processes, thereby revealing

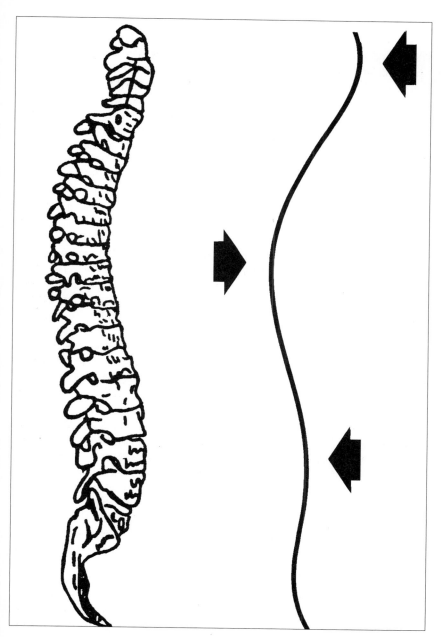

Contours of the Spinal Column

the key to the responses of the soul.

In conclusion, as my first example, I would like to deal with the spine. The spine has always been considered as the axis of the soul. If one looks at the physiological curvatures, one can recognize a curve towards the front in the area of the cervical spine (lordosis), a curvature towards the back in the area of the thoracic spine (kyphosis), and another curvature towards the front in the area of the lumbar spine.

First of all, it is a fact that the frequently-observed symptoms of wear and tear not only cause considerable pain but, at present, have also become a social problem. The cost of treatment is very high and the tendency of these symptoms to become chronic radically increases the numbers of the ill. Official and natural medicine both try to remove pain with their respective methods, but often find it difficult to achieve positive results.

From the viewpoint of natural medicine, man is not attached to the spine; rather, the spine is attached to him. Here, it is necessary to look at man from a holistic point of view, evaluating him on his spirit-soul-body trinity. The realization that a man's posture reveals his inner psychological problems is an ancient one, known to all holistic therapists. Through this knowledge alone, the therapist will receive a first indication as to the person's tensions and their physical expressions.

From the point of view of physics, wear and tear can happen only in places where there is pressure. The questions arises: Where does the pressure come from? Why are only certain sectors of the spine or only the joints affected? One would suppose that laborers who carry heavy loads day in and day out would certainly strain and wear out their spines and joints more than people whose work is less arduous. The reality, however, is quite different. It is especially those who work less strenuously and, at first glance, lead a quite balanced life, and maybe exercise regularly, who have a specific tendency towards the afflictions of wear and tear, mainly of the spine. Furthermore, stress, environmental conditions and, in particular, eating habits are criteria that must be taken into consideration. Yet all these considerations do not indicate a satisfactory resonance. The main reason is that there is no adequate method of treatment for the increasing number of sicknesses of the locomotor system.

The basic considerations of Esogetics say that irregularities of the inner, and of the soul as well, project themselves on the outside where, in their unreality, they manifest their effects. This means, on the one hand, that all alterations of cells, organs and systems are reflected on the outside. On the other hand, because such unrealities within fixed functions must come from somewhere, this means the impulses for change must descend towards the lower from higher levels of consciousness, causing pressure and havoc until the waking consciousness finds its way back to its higher program.

On closer inspection of the curvatures of the spine, one could consider it as a kind of spring which is able to balance out pressure situations. For this task, the curve of the thoracic spine, due to its middle position, is of particular importance. This area is especially susceptible to stress, aggression, fear and melancholy. Here all Functions Circles and their respective keys come together. This is the place where a person "hunches his back." This area, where all man's psychological problems manifest, is one of the great areas of Esogetics. Here, I was able to find a zone which effects man's whole being. It works on upper parts of the body, as well as bringing relaxation to the area of the pelvis and, especially, the abdomen.

At the apex of the spinal curve between the fourth and eighth thoracic vertebrae, all states of pressure manifest themselves and, from there, have an upwards and downwards effect.

To complete this idea, I would like to state that in Esogetics the neck belongs to the mother/female principle, and the lumbar spine to the father/male principle. I will go into this in detail in my next book.

The zone I have discovered between the shoulder blades relaxes the whole body and should be rubbed regularly with Esogetic Herb Oil in the evening before going to sleep. Experiments with this zone have revealed that, within a short time, specific dreams are experienced. People have reported that the content of these dreams is primarily of an instinctive and sexual nature.

The zone between the shoulder blades is closely related to another zone. This zone lies in the middle of the calf in the area where I, with a special somatotopia, have placed the thoracic spine. You can find the first zone by drawing a horizontal line between the two axilla creases of a person sitting in an upright position. The middle point of this line lies on the spine and is the central point. About two finger-widths above and below it, there are two further points. At the edge of the shoulder blades, two points can be located on the horizontal line through the center point. By connecting these points in one's imagination, an ellipse results. This is the zone that should be intensely rubbed with five to eight drops of Esogetic Herb Oil in the evening.

Next, one finds the zone in the middle of the calf, on the right and on the left legs, and also rubs it with three to five drops of the oil. Then one should go to bed. At first the skin will become cold because of the

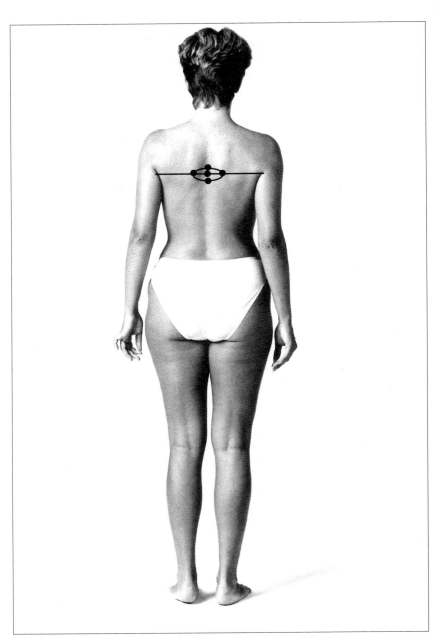

Mental Ellipse between the Shoulder Blades

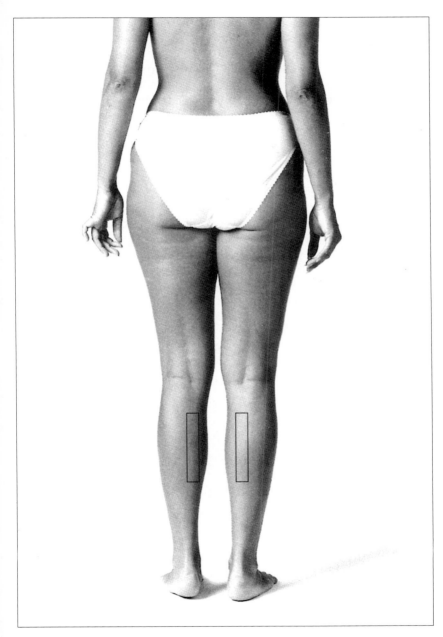

Calf Zone

composition of the oil, but within a few minutes the sensation of coldness will change to a feeling of well-being.

The effect is always dream-producing. At the same time, one's sleep is improved enormously. Try this simple manipulation. If you apply it two to three times a week, you will not only dream, but will also feel, during the day, a different relationship to yourself and to your environment.

So, I have come to the end of this first publication on Esogetics. I am well aware much has remained unsaid. This book is intended to familiarize the reader with the basic principles and the greater correlations. A large number of details, therefore, would have been rather distracting. I have done my best to present simple manipulations from the large number of wonderful discoveries of Esogetics which everyone can apply on himself without harmful side-effects. I hope this book contributes to helping people become freer inside themselves. The awakening of a new strength of soul and spirit, as a result of becoming conscious, makes the individual appear in a totally new light. The person who is on the path of realization will find new specific possibilities to remain healthy and become whole.

In following books, I will present, step by step, the entire range of reflex fields I have found within Esogetics. I will describe all physical aspects related to the spirit and the soul. Many simple instructions will contribute to man taking himself in hand.

ACKNOWLEDGMENTS

At the end of this book I would like to say "thank you":

Thank you to my readers, who impart meaning to this book by as-similating its contents.

Thank you to my friends, who have repeatedly encouraged me to continue on the path of Esogetics and who are a help to me, on this path, through their constructive criticism.

Thank you to my teachers and to all of the people who have given me knowledge and mental stimulation. Without them I would not have been able to ponder things deeply and, therefore, write about them.

Thank you — and there is a heartfelt need for me to express this — to my beloved wife Rosita, who not only helps me convert my ideas into illustrations, but also, through her patience, understanding and compassion, gives me the strength to do what I need to do.

BIBLIOGRAPHY

Bachmann, Gerhard
Die Akupunktur - eine Ordnungstherapie
Heidelberg 1976,2. Auflage, Haug Verlag

Bailey, Alice
Esoterisches Heilen
Verlag Lucis, Genf 1988

Berendt, Joachim-Ernst
Nada Brahma - die Welt ist Klang
RowohltTaschenbuch-Verlag, Reinbek,1986

Berger, Lutz / Pieper, Werner
Braintech - Das Buch, Der grüne Zweig 133
Pieper-Verlag, Löhrbach,1989

Bischko, Johannes
Einführung in die Akupunktur
Heidelberg 1974,5. Auflage, Haug-Verlag

Bischko, Johannes
Akupunktur für Fortgeschrittene
Heidelberg,1974,2. Auflage, Haug-Verlag

Bock, Eleonore
Mystik in den Religionen der Welt
Benziger-Verlag, Zürich,1991

Dethlefsen, Thorwald
Schicksal als Chance
Goldmann Taschenbuchverlag, München,1986

Dethlefsen, Thorwald
Krankheit als Weg
Goldmann Taschenbuchverlag, München,1990

Domnescu, Laurentius
DenkanstöBe in der Parapsychologie
Verlag Hubertus Bollinger, Niddatal,1988

Gleditsch, Jochen M.
Reflexzonen und Somatotopien
Schorndorf 1983, WBV Biologisch-Medizinische Verlagsanstalt

Holler, Johannes
Das neue Gehim
Verlag Bruno Martin, Südergellersen,1989

Hutchison, Michael
Megabrain - Geist und Maschine
Sphinx Medien Verlag,1989, Basel

Johnson, Richard L.
Ich schreibe mir die Seele frei
Verlag Hermann Bauer, Freiburg,1990

Leadbeater, C. W.
Der sichtbare und der unsichtbare Mensch
Verlag Hermann Bauer, Freiburg,1984

Leadbeater, C.W.
Die Chakras
Verlag Hermann Bauer, Freiburg,1986

Mandel, Peter
Lichtblicke in der ganzheitlichen (Zahn)-Medizin
Energetik-Verlag, Bruchsal,1989

Mandel, Peter
Energetische Terminalpunkt-Diagnose
Energetik-Verlag, Bruchsal,1990

Mandel, Peter
Praktisches Handbuch der Farbpunktur
Energetik-Verlag, Bruchsal,1986

Mandel, Peter
Die Akupunkt-Impuls-Therapie
Energetik-Verlag, Bruchsal,1988

Mandel, Peter
Induktionstherapie mit den Frequenzmustern des menschlichen Gehims
Energetik-Verlag, Bruchsal,1991

Popp, Fritz-Albert
Biologie des Lichts
Berlin, Hamburg 1984, Verlag Paul Parey

Riedweg, Franz
Vom Wandel des Denkens in der Medizin
Wiesbaden und München 1977, Limes-Verlas

Riedweg, Franz
Hormonmangel - Initialstörung zahlreicher Krankheitsbilder
Basilopoulos Verlag, Athen,1979

St.John, Robert
Metamorphose - Die pranatale Therapie
Synthesis-Verlag, Essen,1984

Szekely, E. Bordeaux
Das geheime Evangelium der Essener
Verlag Bruno Martin, Südergellersen,1988

Toben, Bob
Raum, Zeitund erweitertes Bewußtsein
Synthesis-Verlag, Essen,1980

Vester, Frederic
Denken, Lemen, Vergessen
dtv, München,1986

Vester, Frederic
Neuland des Denkens
dtv, München, 1984

Voss/Herlinger
Taschenbuch derAnatomie, Bd. I, II und III
Gustav Fischer Verlag, Stuttgart,1986

Wertsch/Schrecke/Küstner
Akupunkturatlas
Schorndorf 1986, 6.Auflage, WBV Biologisch-Medizinische Verlagsanstalt

---

INFORMATION TO ESOGETICS

Energetik-Verlag, Postfach 1023, D-65836 Sulzbach/Taunus
or
MeTePro GmbH, Postfach 2060, D-76610 Bruchsal
or
KAMLA AG, CH-6006 Luzern